GREG'S CHOICE

GREG'S CHOICE

Gregory Clark

Author of
The Best of Gregory Clark

Foreword by
Gillis Purcell

McGRAW-HILL RYERSON LIMITED
Toronto   Montreal   New York   London   Sydney
Mexico   Panama   Johannesburg   Düsseldorf
Rio de Janeiro   Kuala Lumpur   New Delhi   Singapore

Published, 1961

ISBN 0-7700-6025-0

First Paperback Edition, 1968

ACKNOWLEDGMENT

The Publisher and Author are grateful to
Weekend Magazine for permission to reprint
these stories and to Louis Jaques for the
photographs on the jacket and title page.

5 6 7 8 9 10   JD   10 9 8 7 6 5
PRINTED AND BOUND IN CANADA

Foreword

THIS volume comprises slightly less than a year's magazine production by a grizzled sixty-eight-year-old doctor of laws whom the notoriously jealous columnists of this country unanimously regard as the champ.

In addition to these forty-seven weekly columns, which he calls "shorties," he pecks out on a battered typewriter a syndicated daily newspaper feature called "The Packsack."

To maintain this total average output of one widely-read column for each day of the year, this durable observer builds up energy and gathers material by fishing, hunting, birdwatching, browsing around book and hardware stores, studying flowers and stones, and travelling to distant places.

Not solely because his photo, in arresting costume and varied poses, appears atop each column in *Weekend*, he is more frequently recognized on any Canadian street than most politicians, sports figures or TV performers.

And most Canadian politicians, sports figures and TV performers recognize this book's author as a timeless philosopher of incredible good humour whose public projection quietly outreaches them all.

A year ago, after considerable urging, he permitted publication of *The Best of Gregory Clark,* the first collection of his columns to appear in thirty-five years. For the title of this second volume, the confidently modest author rejected his son Greg's suggested *The Second Best of Greg Clark* and his wife's idea, *Bottom of the Barrel.*

He knows, as do his friends and millions of his readers, this can go on and on.

Greg's friends are frequently asked whether the fantastic happenings he relates do really happen. They have learned from experience to accept his stories as only slightly embellished gospel. But their reactions to him vary.

Here are a few, expressed within one winter's week in 1961:

London's most-famed cane-maker: "Over forty years, the most alive and likable customer to come into my shop."[1]

[1] W. G. Cox, son of the late Ben Cox of Oxford Street.

A university president: "Truly a king-size leprechaun."[2]

An all-time hockey great: "He writes my kind of stuff."[3]

A secretary: "A noble master of the sneaky double-play —he can extend a one-cup-of-tea visit with our flattered boss into an hour-long reprieve from work for us grateful girls."[4]

A DSO-winner who was his commanding officer in the First World War: "An unusually intelligent leader who enforced discipline by affection and won respect by unorthodoxy."[5]

An internationally-known guide: "A swell flycaster but his wife's even better."[6]

A fellow war correspondent in the Second World War: "He reduces everything to its most human denominator."[7]

The youngest of his four grandchildren: "Ai, ai, ai!"[8]

A Nobel Prize winner: "One of the most stimulating and vibrant Canadian personalities of our time, as reflected in his life and letters. To know him once is to forget him never."[9]

A television beauty: "In print or in person he can still make a girl forget what's cooking on the stove."[10]

The best left-handed fly-caster in America: "Je l'ai surtout admiré comme pêcheur à la mouche. Il pêche en artiste et il trouve plus de plaisir à leurrer le poisson qu'à le capturer."[11]

A considerably younger columnist: "The old son-of-a-gun is still writing rings around us all."[12]

Put those views through the craftiest of the modern computing machines and this same analysis keeps coming out:

What a wonderful little guy! May his stories ever grow taller!

GILLIS PURCELL
General Manager, The Canadian Press

[2]Dr. G. Edward Hall, University of Western Ontario.
[3]Frank (King) Clancy of Ottawa.
[4]Mary Kibblewhite of Balzac, Alta.
[5]Victor Sifton of Winnipeg.
[6]Doug Robertson of Squilax, B.C.
[7]Doug Amaron of The Canadian Press.
[8]Gregory Thomas Wakabayashi of New York (aged nine months).
[9]L. B. (Mike) Pearson of Canada.
[10]Joyce Davidson, Canadian star now in New York.
[11]Philippe Gagnon, Quebec's assistant deputy minister of game and fisheries.
[12]Bruce West of Toronto *Globe and Mail.*

Contents

The Get-up

IN ONE of those wayside restaurants with the big open glass fronts facing on a gravel parking space off the highway, a happy party of ten people were enjoying their meal.

My wife and I sat modestly at a side table for two. We had just arrived, and it was the only table free.

The large party was a gay one. We were entertained by their spirited chatter and laughter.

"For Heaven's sake!" cried one of the ladies, suddenly. "Look at the get-up of these people."

A car had just drawn up on the gravel patio outside, and five people were uncramping themselves out of it.

They were decidedly outlandish in their garb. The first lady to emerge backward from the car was much too large for her slacks. They were men's slacks, without the generosity in the seat that ladies, particularly family-style ladies, require.

The first man out was thin and bony, with a cigar clamped in his molars. He was wearing a schoolgirl's tuque, of red and green, with a long dangle of it hanging down over his shoulder. His trousers were large loose mackinaw cloth of black and red checks, and he might better have traded them with the lady aforementioned.

"Good grief!" cried one of the ladies in the large party at our next table. "What next!"

The hilarity of the party was infectious. Everybody in the restaurant had turned to crane and get a view of the new arrivals outside.

"Look at that HAT!" screamed the merriest lady who had first spotted them.

From the car, another passenger had eased herself out. On her head was a great big floppy straw hat of the kind you bring home from Nassau, in the Bahamas. Winter being still with us, the hat looked a little out of season. But the lady wearing it was not the season-conscious type. She, too, was large and roomy. She had a heavy woollen lumberjack coat buttoned snugly up around her throat. And on her legs were thigh rubber boots, brand new and shiny.

The man who got out following her was short and fat. He was dressed as a hunter — red cap, brown canvas boots, canvas breeches and half-leg hunting boots. In his arms he carried as ridiculous-looking a little pop-eyed Pekingese as could be imagined.

"Woo-hoo!" howled the large party. "The little fat guy with the dog! I wonder what he hunts?"

"Sssshhh!" pleaded another. "They'll notice you! Don't stare!"

The party outside had bunched together, awaiting the last member, their driver, to emerge.

He was a dandy. He wore a Siwash sweater so small for him that every time he pulled it down in front it popped up behind, and when he gave it a polite little yank behind, it sprang up in front. This he did two or three times as soon as he got out of the car, much to the hysterics of the watchers from within. He had on old-fashioned plus-fours, a bit tight in the seat and loose in the leg; diamond-pattern golf hose, and brown Romeo slippers.

"Who on earth," cried one of the party, "do you suppose they are?"

"And what are they doing, where are they going?"

"It looks," guffawed one of the men, "like the start of a hard-times party."

"Sssshhhh!" went several.

For the five newcomers, after bunching together for

— 2 —

mutual encouragement and looking a little anxiously in the big glass front, moved around to the side, toward the entrance.

There was complete silence as the leader, the woman in the big Nassau straw hat, shoved the door open.

"Hi, Greg!" she hailed.

"Hi, Liz," I responded, standing up.

"How long have you been here?" demanded Liz, leading, and all the rest following. "You must have driven like the wind."

"The girls," I said, "will pull an extra table here."

Liz, Janet, with the tight-fitting pants, Joe, Bumpy and Billy, with the Peke in his arms, gathered cheerfully around.

At the big double table next to us, the hilarious party was silent. More than silent. They were ghastly still. Their faces were purple. They stared at their plates. They cast sidelong glances of horror at one another. Their lunch was ruined. Their day was ruined. They were ruined.

The waitress brought over another table to set beside ours.

Everybody sank into chairs. All but me.

I stepped over and patted the merriest lady of the big party on the shoulder, kindly.

"We're going smelt fishing," I explained.

Finnan Haddie and Lump Sugar

NOT OFTEN do I take a clergyman to lunch. I suppose it is because I am afraid my friends would think I was showing off. But whenever I get the chance to have lunch with the Rev. Dr. Plinkett (that, of course, is not his right name), I jump at it.

He was a friend of my father's, and somehow, when I am with the genial old gentleman, I have the queer feeling my father is still here. Indeed, I always get a table for four, so that there is a chair vacant.

Genial is the word for him. A rugged-headed, rosy-faced, energetic old gentleman of the cloth.

We were well into our lunch, both of us partaking (I I believe that is the word) of good thick finnan haddie done in milk, with scalloped potatoes and stewed tomatoes with plenty of onion, and we were discussing a fishing trip he had been on when he was twelve years old, which would be sixty-four years ago, on which he filled his mother's wash boiler with speckled trout. Them, he was telling me, were the days.

At this point, there passed our table a young couple, the mother carrying a pretty little girl of about two years of age, all dressed up in the doll-like finery which little girls of two can still wear.

She was a little beauty.

As they passed, the young father paused and said hello to my companion.

The Rev. Dr. Plinkett scrambled to his feet and greeted the young couple most heartily, and introduced me to them.

"I married them!" exulted the Rev. Doctor. "And did you ever see a more beautiful consequence?"

I was glad of the excuse to touch the baby's hand. She gave me a lazy look and then turned her back, as girls of two have already learned to do.

Dr. Plinkett, with that innate generosity of his calling, reached down to the table and took a cube of sugar from our sugar bowl and handed it ceremoniously to the little darling. The little darling promptly seized it and put it in her mouth.

The young couple moved on to their table and we sat down. Parsons apparently do not know that a square lump of sugar is one of the unhandiest things to put in your mouth, even if you are an adult. It is hard. It won't fit into any particular nook or cranny of your mouth. Its shape inclines it to wobble and pop around inside.

The Rev. Doctor's back was to his young friends. He could not see that by the time the mother had got the baby seated in the high chair which the restaurant provided, the little girl was already dribbling profusely. The mother was hastily trying to stem the flow with her hanky.

She tried to get the little girl to surrender the lump. But the little darling let out a closed-lip scream and started to wriggle violently in protest.

A wise and motherly waitress hurried up with a table napkin. But the bow of ribbon with which the pretty little hat was fastened, under the chin, was already sodden.

Mother, daddy and the waitress combined to undo the ribbon and get the hat off. The little girl fought and twisted, her mouth tightly shut.

Daddy squatted down and begged for the sugar. In order to say "No" most emphatically, the little girl had to open her mouth slightly, and down all over her pretty white coat dribbled another generous cascade. With hasty fingers, the mother, the daddy and the waitress struggled to un-button the coat and hoist it off.

Dr. Plinkett had reached the point in his story of how his mother used to cook speckled trout in an iron frying pan eighteen inches across, that was an heirloom from her pioneer grandmother. But I was not able strictly to keep my mind on what he was saying.

The little girl, leaning back in her high chair, was sitting tight-lipped and belligerent.

Her parents seated themselves, distractedly. The waitress took a couple of exploratory swipes with the napkin under the baby's chin.

Her dress was one of those lovely, filmy, flowered organdies, a spray of a dress, a wisp, a garland, a chaplet of a dress. And it had a sweet, crisp frill around the neck. The darling buried her chin in the frill.

"Please?" begged the mother.

The baby put her hand in her mouth and kindly brought forth a handful of melted sugar. With a leap, mother, daddy and the waitress all grabbed for her hand; but the little girl was quicker. She wiped heartily, both hands, across the front of her dress.

And there, his back to the tragedy, sat dear old Dr. Plinkett, full of finnan haddie and feeling he had done his good turn for the day.

Cranberries

RED HAWK, who has a Christian name as well, which we never use, is an Indian with no trace of French or English blood in his veins. He has the beautiful copper-red colour that distinguishes his race from all others.

You can see a little way into the blackest eye of Italian or Arab, Spaniard or Negro, Japanese or Korean. But you can't see a millionth of an inch into the eye of the Red Indian. Indeed, your vision bounces back from an Indian's. It has always been a mystery to me, especially after the long years of my acquaintance with Red Hawk, that we white men were ever able to conquer, let alone cheat, flimflam and swindle the noble redman as we have.

Red Hawk wrote me that he had located an albino ruffed grouse, or partridge, on the reservation, and would show it to me if I cared. His Indian reservation is one of those inland from the great Georgian Bay. I wrote at once to Red Hawk setting a day and place some two weeks later for a rendezvous. You have to do this with him, because, like Napoleon Bonaparte, he has observed that if you do not open your letters for three days, it is astonishing how few of them need to be answered. So Red Hawk will often leave a letter on the shelf of his cabin for a whole week, unopened. He likes to wonder what is in it, for a while.

"It is usually so much more interesting to wonder what is in it than to find what is in it," he says.

On the appointed day, I drove the two hundred miles to the village on the highway where I was to meet Red Hawk on the general-store steps at four P.M. To reach the reservation, we had a five-mile walk, and arrived at his humble shanty just at dark. Red Hawk has a very low opinion of white men, and would rather not be seen entertaining them by his fellow-Indians. We talked in low tones by the stove until bedtime, and were up bright and early to get out into the hardwood bush where the albino partridge had been seen half a dozen times by my friend. This has been a wonderful year, hereabouts, for acorns, especially the white oak; and the partridge are fat and not too shy.

We had flushed four or five normal birds, without seeing the snow-white one, when Red Hawk suddenly halted and signalled me to hush.

He raised his head, like a buck deer, and strained to listen.

"Somebody," he hissed to me, gleefully, "is in the cranberry marsh."

"Indians, maybe?"

"Too noisy," said Red Hawk. "Come on. Follow me. Quiet, now."

Up a hill and along a rocky ridge he led me in great stealth. We came out on a pine-clad cliff overlooking the mile-long cranberry marsh, which is one of the richest features of the reservation.

Three figures were visible on the far edge of the marsh, industriously bent.

"Shogenosh," breathed Red Hawk, deeply. White men.

"What do you do?" I whispered. "Call the Provincials?"

"Ssshhh!" said Red Hawk.

From amid the screen of pines, we watched the intruders. White men are not allowed on the reservations except on proper business, such as trying to see an albino partridge.

"Do you recognize them?" I asked.

"I think so. Three bums from down on the Bay."

"Well, why don't you yell, and scare them off?"

Red Hawk just gave me a long opaque stare and a slow white grin.

He continued to watch, from our perch.

"They're using scoops," he said. "Boxes with teeth sawed along the edge."

I saw one of the three stand up and gaze around. He was carrying a burlap sack, like a potato bag.

"He's got a bag half full," I mentioned.

"O.K., come on," said Red Hawk. "And don't make a sound. Don't cough. Don't crack any sticks."

He led me off the cliff and along the slope of the ridge in a wide detour that would bring us out on the far side of the marsh. From time to time he would leave me in the leafless underbrush while he scouted forward for a glimpse of the bog. Finally he beckoned me forward with gestures to indicate great stealth. I crept forward beside him.

We were now within fifty yards of the three men working swiftly in the marsh. They were bent very low, their shoulders moving as they swept up the berries in their toothed boxes and emptied them into the bags. They kept raising their heads every moment or two to glance about. Whenever they moved to a new position they tried to keep under cover of the clumps or buttonbush and bayberry with which the marsh was filled.

We had been watching less than five minutes when one of the three stood up and started for shore, dragging his potato sack of berries behind him. On reaching the rocky edge of the marsh, he sat down and proceeded to tie up the mouth of his sack with string.

"When I stand up," whispered Red Hawk in my ear, "don't you follow. You just stand up and put your hands on your hips like this."

"Arms akimbo," I said.

"That's the way officials stand," breathed my friend. "You just stand there, staring, with your hands on your hips."

"Got it," I agreed.

The other two pickers, bent low, started for shore. When they were within a few paces, Red Hawk stood up.

"Hey!"

The three froze.

"Don't you know this is an Indian reservation?"

Silence.

"You come with this officer and me to the town now," said Red Hawk, going forward.

Silence.

"Or," in a deeper and more resonant voice, "you leave them berries and git!"

The three of them dropped the sacks, gathered into a little tight group, and got.

When the sounds of them hustling through the brush died away, Red Hawk sighed happily.

"Every year," he gloated, "I let the white men pick my berries for me."

We carried the three bags to a temporary and safe hiding place and then went and saw the albino partridge.

It was beautiful, mystic, like a spirit bird, just as Red Hawk had told me.

The Live Wire

EXUBERANCE is one of the better human failings. But it has its limits. If you want to know why I am going around with a bandaged hand, I will quietly tell you.

Quietly, moderately, without malice, I will tell you. I was at a cocktail party given in honour of a rising celebrity in the publishing world. If you are not familiar with cocktail parties, I should tell you that always, always about twice as many people turn up as were expected. These parties usually run from 5 to 7 p.m., by which time many of the gathering have thought of something better to do and, anyway, the canapes on the big trays are all gone except for a few of the untastier one, like damp sardines on small squares of cold, humid toast.

But about 6 p.m., the hotel suite in which the party is being held fairly blasts with the sound of close-packed guests. It is a chivaree. It is a hullabaloo. Nobody can move, except by sidling. Everybody is looking over everybody else's shoulder at somebody else they wish they were stalled with.

I was standing modestly among the wallflowers near the door, talking to three strangers, all of us mistaking each other for somebody else, when I saw, bulging through the jam, an old friend I hadn't seen for five or six years.

He is the exuberant type. He was born exuberant. He was a hugger from his cradle. He practised slapping his father's back from infancy. He was giving three cheers before he could toddle. He whoops. He hollers. At cocktail parties, he greets six people at once. He shakes hands with both hands. To him, a cocktail party is a square dance.

He is a type you find among salesmen, advertising men, greeters and joiners. You seldom meet the type among bank managers, civil servants and chartered accountants.

With some delight, I watch him plunging and gyrating through the solid company, shouldering, bulging, hand-shaking, back-slapping, nudging, hooting, guffawing. It was interesting to watch the outraged expressions of those he jostled on his way. He fairly glistened with joy. Any minute, he would see me.

I was smoking a cigarette, which I had in my right hand, projecting, half-smoked, outward from between my index and second finger.

The wallflower on my left was just showing me a snapshot of his wife and two kiddies. It was 6.30 p.m., which is the family-snapshot hour at cocktail parties.

My exuberant friend caught me unawares. He sprang. He bunted through four layers of humanity to get me.

"GREG!" he shouted, from the flank.

And he seized both my hands in a tremendous clasp. His left hand, large, muscular, damp, closed upon my right. I could feel my cigarette sizzling as he crushed it on to the back of my hand.

He had it in the palm of his.

Wide-eyed, joyous, mouth wide in the very act of exulting at the sight of me, his expression suddenly was transfigured into one of anguish, and from his open mouth came a roar of pain.

"Yow!" he yelled, releasing my hand.

We both hastily examined our wounds, blowing and dusting.

I just wanted to stand there and be mad.

"Here! Hey! Come on!" he bellowed, seizing me by the elbow and propelling me toward the door of the suite.

"Look," I said, "just a second . . ."

"Come on! We'll find the first-aid kit."

He had me in an iron, St. John Ambulance grip, by the elbow. Out the hall we went, down the empty corridor.

"Girl in the hall, here," he commanded, "sitting at a desk. She'll know. There ought to be a first-aid kit on every floor. Big, modern hotel . . ."

I tried to drag back.

"My dear boy!" he hooted. "Right along here!"

When we turned the corner of the corridor, there was no girl at the desk. My, how empty the corridor was.

"We'll go down the elevator . . ."

"Now, just a minute!"

A waiter appeared, shoving a dinner wagon loaded with somebody's supper.

"Waiter!" he shouted. "Quick! Butter!"

The astonished waiter watched as my friend whipped aside the fresh white napkins, snatched a pat of butter off a plate, seized my hand, smeared the butter hastily on my burn, and then tenderly smeared it on the palm of his hand.

"Butter!" he boomed. "Nothing like butter for burns. Come on. Let's go back to the party . . ."

But no. Quietly, moderately, without malice, I said no. I had to be on my way.

So down the hall he strode, eager for the fray, and I went the other way; going home in the bus, with my hankie wrapped around my hand. And when I got home, my wife put this bandage on it.

A Barl of Apples

"HOW," shouted my aged friend Dandy Daniels over the phone, "would you like to go halvers with me on a couple of barls of apples?"

Dandy, who was born somewhere back in the eighteen-seventies, speaks the old Ontario English. He calls a barrel a "barl", and a mirror a "murr." It is the way Ontarians spoke before they packed up and left to populate the Western prairies, and before the Maritimers moved in on Ontario with their parsons, bankers, lawyers and businessmen to instruct Ontario how to speak the Queen's English. (Victoria, that was.)

"Barrels of apples, Dandy!" I protested. "My dear old friend, they haven't sold apples in barrels for years and years."

"Don't quibble!" barked Dandy.

I then realized the old gentleman merely wanted a drive in the country at this delectable time of year. When he calls me up, he usually has a good excuse.

He and Hortense, who has been his housekeeper for forty years, were waiting on the porch of their small tidy house when I arrived in my car right after lunch.

"Apples!" said Dandy, creaking in beside me in the front seat.

"He wants a barrel of Northern Spies," said Hortense, creaking into the back seat, "a barrel of Greenings and a barrel of Russets."

"You just sit and view the scenery," yelled Dandy. "I'll do the talking."

Hortense unscrewed her hearing aid from her ear and relaxed back for a pleasant afternoon.

"Dandy," I said, as we took off for the suburbs, "you know perfectly well there hasn't been a barrel of apples seen in these parts for nearly half a century."

"I mind the time," said Dandy, "when EVERYBODY had three barls of apples in their cellar by this time of year. A barl of Northern Spies, a barl of Greenings for pies and apple sauce, and a barl of Russets for the bowl on the parlor table."

"And Snows?" I checked.

"No," corrected Dandy, "you didn't get a barl of Snows. They wouldn't keep. You just got a couple of bushels of Snows and ate 'em the first two or three weeks. But you kept the other three barls right through to February and even March."

"Cellars were colder in those days," I suggested.

"Apples," said Dandy, "were APPLES in those days. Now, with all this fertilizer and cortisone and antibiotics and stuff they plow into the ground around apple trees, they won't keep a month."

"Not antibiotics, Dandy."

"Well, whatever it is," said Dandy. "New and improved. Why, back in the days when this was God's country, an apple was so crisp, it cracked when you bit it. Juice exploded out of it. It smelt like a rose. And tasted like a . . . like a . . . Well, there isn't anything that describes the way an apple used to taste before these geophysicists got after them."

"Not geophysicists," I said. "Arboriculturalists."

"You drive," said Dandy. "I'll do the talking."

So I drove. And hardly had we passed out beyond the suburbs before we came to roadside stands at the lane entrances to farms and around service stations, with pumpkins, squash and other autumnal victuals, and baskets of apples shining like Christmas ornaments piled high and stacked along the ground.

"Hey! Ho!" yelled Dandy. "Pull up!"

Out we got, Hortense and all, and inspected the beautiful produce.

"Got any barls?" demanded Dandy.

The young fellow tending the stand was from Holland or the Ukraine or some place and couldn't make out what a barl was. The basket Dandy liked best, of big, florid apples of some species which had apparently been grown for their cosmetic virtues, was $1.10.

"A dollar ten!" cried Dandy. "We used to get a BARL for $1.10!"

The young man was not impressed. He was selling Hortense three butternut squash for a quarter.

"Can I sample these?" demanded Dandy, indicating the $1.10 basket.

The young man hastily got a loose one for Dandy from under the counter.

Dandy bit it.

"Thpoo!" he said as he spat out the first bite. "No, THANKS!"

But he carried the apple back into the car, and as we drove along, he ate it with the loud cracks the elderly, with loose dentures, employ in demolishing an apple.

"Like punk!" snorted Dandy, as he flung the well-trimmed core out the window. "Whoa! Pull up!"

And we hauled in to another roadside stand.

Here Dandy went through the routine of inspecting the wares, recounting what apples used to be like, how much they used to cost, and got another sample—this time a fine McIntosh Red right from the middle of a basket.

"Thpoo!" he exploded out the first bite. "No, THANKS!"

And we got back in the car and he ate that apple right down to the seeds.

"Like eating cardboard!" he declared as he tossed away the core.

We stopped at six or seven roadside stands before we got well out into the country and found the orchards in our richest apple-growing region. In one of them, we could see men loading hampers and bushel baskets of apples on to trucks at a loading platform up the lane.

"Ah, here we are!" cried Dandy. "Turn in."

"Who's the farmer here?" he hollered as we drew up at the trucks.

"I'm the foreman," said a middle-aged man on the platform, "if that's what you want. The farmer doesn't live here. He lives in town."

"What kind of apples have you got?" called Dandy.

"None for sale," said the foreman. "One of the big chain stores has bought all our crop for the next eight years."

"Well," demanded Dandy, "how do I get a barl of apples? Can you tell me that?"

"Go to a chain store," said the foreman, picking up another hamper, "and fill a barl with them."

"Well, I asked a civil question," yelled Dandy.

"No offence, Dad," replied the foreman.

"Got any samples?" asked Dandy.

"Help yourself," said the foreman, "from that busted hamper over there."

Dandy got out and picked six: one for Hortense, one for me, and four for himself.

"Let's," said Dandy, as we got out on the highway again, "turn off on some measly side road and find some old skinflint of a farmer with a miserable old orchard full of gnarly trees that have never seen any modern improvements and get some old-fashioned apples with scabs on them, and lopsided."

But about three miles up the road, Dandy complained of cramps in his stomach. Shortly after, he began to belch much more loudly than one would expect of so feeble an old man.

"He's et mine," said Hortense, who also speaks Old Ontario.

So we stopped and put Dandy in the back seat where he could lie down, and Hortense got in the front seat with me, and we drove home.

"Apples!" muttered old Dandy, as we assisted him up his front steps. "Thpooooo!"

Decoration

SOME PEOPLE just can't leave life alone.

They have to decorate it. My father was one of them.

"Your youngest brother," he said to me one evening, "wants a pair of binoculars for his birthday."

"I guess he's old enough," I reflected. "Seventeen."

"He's been hinting around," said Dad.

"Seems to me," I said, "he's got a gun, and he's a bit of a naturalist. Yes, binoculars WOULD be good."

"Expensive, aren't they?" thought Dad.

"Well, they run all prices," I said. "Around $30 you can get a serviceable pair. But they go way over $100."

"Wow!" said my parent. "What could you do for around $75?"

So I was instructed to purchase in a day or so a good pair of binoculars that would last Arthur for half his life.

The following morning, my father phoned around seven and suggested we walk to the office. On fine winter mornings such as this, we often met at a mutually convenient corner and walked the twenty minutes downtown for exercise and for the kind of lively conversation that can be enjoyed while walking.

When he reached the corner of Queen and York, which, in those days was the centre of the second-hand and junk-store trade, my father slowed down and we began looking in the curious, jumbled windows of these dirty little shops. He was that kind of a man. Interested in every mortal thing.

"I think," he said, "I saw some very handsome opera glasses in here one time . . ."

"Oh, Dad!" I protested.

— 19 —

"Aha!" he cried, pointing into the dusty jumble of second-hand carpenter's tools, hammers, L-squares, padlocks, as well as gew-gaws, cheap vases, old candy boxes full of rusty bolts.

And up in one corner were half a dozen ridiculous-looking opera glasses in a pile, with a little scrap of paper: "Special $9.95."

They were silver-coloured white metal embossed with classic Greek figures like a Wedgwood vase. The tawdriest things imaginable. I could guess what their magnification might be.

"Come on," said my father.

I followed him in.

From the back of the dim, cluttered shop an elderly man came forward like a vulture about to take wing. He had his hat and coat on, which increased his vulturine appearance.

"Good morning," said my father, cheerily. "I would like to look at those beautiful silver opera glasses you have in the window."

"Ah, yes!" croaked the store keeper. "Wonderful bargain. I got them at a bankrupt sale. Worth ten times the price."

He extracted a pair from the window and handed them reverently to my father.

"Charming," said he, handing them to me.

They were awful. Cheap white metal, stamped in a classic design. I went to the door and looked through them. They didn't magnify at all. All they did was concentrate the gaze.

"How much did you say?" asked my father.

"A bargain, if ever," said the store-keeper. "Nine ninety-five! Can you believe it?"

My father examined the glasses carefully.

"I'll give you," he said, "five dollars!"

"Five!" wailed the store-keeper. "Why I'm practically giving them away at $9.95!"

"Five," said Dad.

"Look," said the vulture, in a heart-broken voice, "seven-fifty. That's the very bottom. That's the . . ."

"Four!" said my Dad.

You would think my father had struck the man. He recoiled as from a blow. His eyes glared.

"Four!" he cried. "FOUR you say! You said FIVE! Now you say FOUR!"

"Well," said my father, "you came down from $9.95 to $7.50. If you can come down, so can I."

The man looked as if a blasphemy had been uttered. He rolled his eyes to heaven.

"Look!" he whispered hoarsely. "You ain't supposed to go DOWN. You are supposed to come UP! I said seven-fifty."

"I say four," said my father.

The man turned his back and walked three paces back into the tangled shadows. He appeared to be pulling himself together.

Then he came back.

"Listen!" he said. "Six dollars! SIX DOLLARS! That's the absolute last!"

"Two-fifty," said my father, calmly.

The man fairly screamed.

"UP!" he cried. "You got to come UP!"

"No," said my father. "I don't believe in that principle at all. If you can come down, so can I. Two-fifty."

And he set the glasses on the counter.

From his pocket he drew two dollar bills and two quarters and laid them beside the glasses.

"Take it," he said, "or leave it."

"You're crazy!" said the store-keeper. "You're CRAZY!"

"Absolutely," said my father, standing pat.

Never have I seen such agony as the store-keeper suffered. Here was not only blasphemy; here was subversion, here was heresy, here was a shattering destruction of the very fundamentals of human intercourse.

He took the money with an almost violent gesture.

My Dad took the glasses and out we went.

That noon, I called at an optical store and bought Arthur's $75 binoculars and delivered them to Dad in his office.

As was customary when there was a birthday in our family, we all assembled at Dad's for breakfast at 8 a.m. to wish the celebrant many happy returns and watch him unwrap his gifts.

Dad had the binoculars hidden in the pantry. But conspicuous in the pile around Arthur's place at the breakfast table was an ornate package containing the phony opera glasses.

Trying to look unsuspecting of his wishes come true, Arthur at last undid the box. Out came the ridiculous tin opera glasses.

"Oh, Dad!" he exclaimed. "Thank YOU!"

And the astonished lad went to the window to try the opera glasses at the surroundings and to hide his feelings.

We all felicitated Arthur on his happy gift. He passed them around to us, to admire. The boy was just about speechless with dismay.

"Oh," said Dad. "Where's that other box?"

And he got the other from the pantry. Arthur, with trembling hands, undid it, and there were the REAL binoculars, big, black.

Now, this is the full story of just one small incident.

Sometimes, I have thought Dad was making sure we would always remember him. Well, we always have.

But now that I am old, I have changed my mind.

I think he was just having a wonderful time, each hour, every day, decorating it.

Gotcha

I SAW THIS HAT, a lady's hat, come bounding and bouncing across the icy intersection.

From under the brim of my hat, with my head bent against the bitter gale, I glimpsed it coming. I saw five or six people, both men and women, from among the downtown throng of the intersection, make a grab for it as it sailed, bounced, curved on the wind.

In fact, I saw one man—and this is important to the record—I saw one man try to stamp on it as it whirled past his feet.

But the wild January wind picked it up just in time, and it rose a yard in the air and came straight for me.

It was a pretty hat, roughly about the size of a pie plate. Against the dirty background of King and Yonge streets, with its leaden ice-coated pavement and the bleak, tall walls of the banks, their stone lashed with sleet, the hat was a pretty thing.

It was pink. It had soft pink feathers on it, though I did not perceive its delicacy at the moment.

It had little sequins sewn here and there amid the soft pink feathers.

You see the situation. The grey January day. The wild midday gale, whirling, lashing the intersection. All those people, heads down, pushing both ways across the intersection. And this lady's hat coming out of nowhere, whirling, evading, side-slipping, banking amid all the perils of street car, bus, automobile and pedestrian.

Now I must interrupt the programme for a moment to explain to you that I am a gentleman, so to speak, of the old school. I carry a stick. What is more, I am an old soldier, trained for years to act, and to act with instant decision. Furthermore, I am a sportsman, familiar with the strike of the muskellunge, with the sudden explosion of the partridge from amid the autumn leaves, and with the paralyzing bound of the buck deer in the tag alders. All these things, over the years, enter into a man's very nature.

Therefore, I throw myself on the mercy of my readers when I relate just how I reacted to the situation when I saw those five or six people making wild grabs at the hat, when I saw that man make a stamp at it with his foot.

It lifted a yard in the air and came straight at me.

As it neared, it swerved to my right side.

With one swift stroke, I swiped it down with my walking stick.

"Gotcha!" I cried.

And there, in the middle of the intersection, on that grey leaden dirty ice, all wrecked and crumpled like a tender bird, lay the lady's beautiful pink hat.

"Well played, sah!" cried an Englishman in the uniform of a commissionaire, and passed smartly on.

But as I stood there, looking down in horror at the little pink ruin on the cruel pavement, others did not pass on. They paused and looked with me.

"Holy smoke!" said one.

"Wow!" said another.

Two office girls, hunched in their collars, let out little screams.

And the lady who owned the hat—oh, about thirty, and clutching to her throat a smart short mink coat, her hair flying—rushed into the midst of us and snatched the poor pink wreckage to her bosom.

"You HIT it!" she cried.

"Madam, I . . ."

"With your STICK!" she wept. "I saw you hit it."

"Lady, it was going to be run over by a car, by a . . ."

"You STRUCK it!" she repeated, horror in her eyes, her voice.

"I saw him, too," accused one of the girls.

"It was deliberate," announced a fat man with a red nose.

The lights changed, and the intersection became loud with car horns. We hastily moved, and though I had been going in the other direction, I chivalrously followed the lady with the pink remains. So did several others. We formed a cluster on the crowded sidewalk in the wind.

"My dear young lady," I said, "come along. I'll buy you a new one."

"You couldn't, you!" she cried, and her eyes were wet.

"Aw, now," I protested. "After all, all I was trying to do was capture it, intercept it . . ."

"You HIT it!" she said, unbelief still in her voice, "With your stick!"

And she fondled the little smudged bundle of pink with the sequins in it. Strange, the love of a woman for a hat.

One of the girls moved and stood beside her.

"Take him up!" she declared loudly. "Make him buy you a new one."

"He couldn't," said the young woman. "It was made specially. I'm on my way to a luncheon at the hotel."

She ran her hand distractedly through her hair, which was a bit wind-tossed.

"You'll have to have a hat," said the girl.

We were being bunted by the crowd on the corner. "After all," I announced, "I saw another man try to STAMP on it!"

"Phooo!" said the girl beside the young lady, and they

moved back out of the wind into the shelter of the bank corner.

I glanced about. The fat man was gone. Nobody was paying any attention. I decided to drop the whole matter.

Out to the curb I stepped. The wind made a grab. My hat blew off. On its edge, it spun out into the traffic.

A car squashed it.

"Goody!" came a shrill cry from the corner of the bank. I think it was that girl, that other one, the interloper.

I did not pick up my hat. I did not even glance down at it.

I went straight across and into the hat shop and bought a new one.

That's the difference between a man and a woman re hats.

The Kind Heart

THE TRAIN was twenty minutes late getting into the Union Station. That is why everybody was in a cranky, pushy mood, I suppose.

Personally, I am never in a hurry. I am a toddler, though elderly.

As I got down on the platform and picked up my suitcase, the passengers from other cars were shoving past. They bunted me.

When I am bunted, I don't get angry. I just sneer at their backs.

I got in the procession and was bunted along, travelling bags bumping my legs, briefcases jagging me in the ribs, tall men's raincoats, flung over their arms, knocking my hat sideways.

Young executives shoved me aside to get ahead of me on the steps leading down to the main concourse. Stout ladies from the parlour cars hipped or bellied me out of the path.

Ahead of me there was some obstruction on the stairs. I could hear a child crying.

The procession, with scant consideration, eddied around the obstruction.

And there, on the step below me, I saw this young mother, with one baby about a year old held up on her left shoulder. And with her right hand she was holding the hand of a little boy about two years old, AND a suitcase.

Well, I had my own suitcase.

So I pushed on the step beside them, letting the bunters behind me mutter and grumble, and in my cheeriest voice I said:

"Aha, now! Give me the little fellow's hand, and I'll help him down the steps, eh?"

"Oh, thank you," said the young mother.

And I was glad. Because she was a very pretty little thing, all damp and tousled from the journey. I figure she had been in a day coach.

It was the baby up on her left shoulder who was crying. It was a weary little baby. Its head rolled. Its eyes were red, its cheeks flushed from being waked.

"Yah-waw!" it wailed.

The little boy had given me his hand with the greatest unconcern. And when I stooped out and had a look at him, as we stepped patiently from step to step down the dim-lit passage, I could see why. He was practically walking in HIS sleep.

"Atta boy," I coached him. We stumbled down, the procession pushing and staring at us with impatience.

We got down into the tiled corridor leading to the concourse.

"There now," said I, very granddaddy.

The young mother smiled wanly at me.

"We've come all the way from Winnipeg," she said.

"Let's rest," I suggested, setting down my suitcase, but holding the little boy's hand while the crowd thinned past.

She set down her suitcase. And I then observed that in the hand of the arm with which she was holding up the head-wobbling infant she was also carrying a bulging paper shopping bag.

"Aw, here!" I protested. "Let me have that."

"Thank you," said she, letting me have the shopping bag and shifting the baby to cradle it across her arm.

It cuddled to her and fell asleep.

"O.K.?" I said.

So we picked up suitcases, and I held the little boy's

hand with the same hand with which I held the cords of the shopping bag. Perfect.

We toddled down the passage and into the concourse. The last of the throng of passengers were moving grumpily away; friends were greeting; wives with car keys in their hands were welcoming husbands; husbands in shirt sleeves were sheepishly kissing wives (summer bachelors, I suppose, glad to have them back); all the usual tired scene of the end of a journey at ten P.M. of a hot summer night.

"There now!" I said, when we reached an open space in the concourse, and setting my suitcase down.

"I am ever so much obliged to you," said the young mother, setting her suitcase down and wiping the hair back from her forehead. She was a weary one, sure enough. She sagged.

"Is someone meeting you?" I asked, solicitously.

"I'll just take the children into the rest room for a jiffy," she replied. "Would you mind the shopping bag a moment?"

"Why, certainly, my dear," I assured her.

Picking up her suitcase and hooking the little boy's hand with one finger, she went over and in the door of the rest room.

As a rule, I like to nip out and catch a taxi before they are all gone. But kind hearts are more than coronets, or even taxis. So I propped the shopping bag against my suitcase. And, leaning on my stick, I watched the dwindling crowd with amiable eye. It is a comfort to do the decent thing, once in a while. It gives you a condescending eye on the rest of mankind.

Three or four minutes went by. The crowd thinned out until there were only a few sleepers on the benchers and the odd lonesome conductor wandering by with his homeward bag.

Five or six minutes went by.

A redcap I know shoved his empty hand truck past.

"Hey, Joe?" I said. "Are you allowed to look in that ladies' rest room?"

"Why?"

"Well, a young mother asked me to mind this shopping bag while she took her kids in there."

"Oh, sure," said Joe, redcaps being sort of above reproach in most things. He went over and gently shoved the door open.

He bent in.

"Nobody here," he called.

"What?" said I. "She didn't come out! Is there a back entrance?"

"No," said Joe. "Maybe she came out when you weren't looking."

"But she left this bag," I protested.

"What's in it?" asked Joe, stooping to look.

It was stuffed full.

"I tell you what," said he. "The Travellers Aid office. Right over there. She'll take charge of it."

"Thanks, Joe."

I carried my suitcase and the shopping bag over to the Travellers Aid. A pleasant lady in a blue hat was just closing up for the night.

"A young mother," I said, "whom I helped off the train, asked me to mind this bag for a minute while she took the children into the rest room. And she didn't come back."

"Dear me," said the Travellers Aid lady.

I hoisted the bag up to her counter.

She explored it briefly.

"Dear me," she said.

"May I leave it?" I asked.

"You may," said the Travellers' Aid lady, with a smile.

"And if it isn't claimed within thirty days, you can have it."

From her expression, I think I know what was in the shopping bag.

So I went out; and am glad to tell you there was one taxi left.

Foiled

WHEN the porter conducted me down to my reservation, seat 5 in the chair car, I glanced covertly around at the chairs adjacent. It was an eight-hour journey ahead of me, the whole long day. I looked forward to spending the trip snoozing, gazing out the window at the coming of spring, reading a little bit, snoozing some more. And everything could be spoiled if, in one of the seats beside me or across from me, some chatter-box of a casual acquaintance were to be my neighbour, who would gas and blather away, mile after mile, hour after hour.

What might be worse, of course, would be two middle-aged women with brand new hairdos, on their way to some convention, who, in strident society voices, would ruin the whole journey by tirelessly interrupting each other, debating their plans. It was with pleasure I noted, with my first cautious glance, that my immediate neighbours were complete strangers, already deeply immersed in their news-papers, and not at all the chatty type. The seat directly across from me, chair six, was not yet occupied. I hoped for the best.

I got a couple of magazines and a good fishing book out of my bag and disposed the bag and my coat up in the rack. I shook out the morning paper, swung my chair firmly around to face out the window, and snuggled down for a pleasant and restful eight hours.

Just as the train started, I noticed out of the corner of my eye, the porter approaching with a bag. Behind him came an elderly man. I was lucky. He was a complete stranger. With a little shrug of content, I snuggled deeper in my seat. He was in chair six.

I heard him thank the porter quietly. His voice was deep and kindly. A beautiful voice.

After watching out the window at the passing suburbs in the bright morning, I decided to swing my chair around casually and have a look at chair six. He was just lighting a cigarette and had one of those 35-cent paper back novels laid ready on his knee.

His head was shaggy, gray and noble. His profile was intensely interesting, a strong curved nose, splendid rugged forehead, humorous mouth. His eyes glanced out from under bristly brows. And he was tanned, even at this time of year, a deep, grained brown. Not a Florida tan, I thought to myself. This is a man from the North. Perhaps he is some famous mining geologist from Yellowknife.

His tweed suit was rough and costly. My glance ran down to his boots: they were those soft, walnutty ankle boots, obviously hand-made. By Lob, of London, I bet myself, or at least by Tricker, also of London.

He picked up the cheap paper novel and opened it with a sigh of pleasant relaxation. The more I looked at this magnificent old man, the more excited I became. Across his chest he wore an old-fashioned watch chain from which dangled some curious charm. On his left hand, I saw the iron finger ring of the Engineers. There could be no doubt about it; across from me sat one of the great Canadians. I cleared my throat and rattled my newspaper. He was already lost in page one of his tawdry novel.

After a while, I swung around and tried to enjoy the passing fields and woods. But I felt easier when turned slightly, so as to be able to seize an opportunity, if it presented itself, of opening a conversation. He swung his chair around to face out his window.

An hour went by, two hours. He never took his eyes off his book. And he read dreadfully slowly. What a way, I thought, for a man of his stamp to waste his time, reading trash. I dipped into my fishing book. I glanced through magazines. I coughed, sighed. When he goes to lunch in the dining car, I figured, I will follow, in the hope of getting to the same table. But he fell asleep at lunch time; and after a long wait, I went in without him. He came in, to another table, just as I was preparing to leave.

The miles, the hours clicked by. I never remember a more restless journey. Not once did the distinguished old man meet my glance or indicate the slightest awareness of me. He was literally sunk in his book.

We neared the journey's end. I thought perhaps he would finish the book in time for five minutes, ten minutes, so that I could at least discover who and what he was. But it was a race between him and the book and the train. It was a dead heat. We lumbered into the station. People were all putting on their coats, as was I.

He finished the book and tossed it aside, stood up with a bright, kindly gaze around. He smiled at me, I at him, as he put on his hat.

"Do you know," he said, "I believe I have read that damned book before!"

And I never did find out who and what he was.

Lilacs

I HAVE it all figured out. The reason most of us don't make friends too easily with our neighbours is that we see too much of one another. Front door, back door, winter, summer, we always have our eyes on one another, and it is hard to create those illusions which are the essence of true friendship.

Besides, all kinds of cockeyed things happen.

For nearly two years, the house on the other side of our block, whose garden abutted on ours, was vacant. Due to some litigation, it stood empty; its garden went to weeds, mulleins, burdocks. But, oh, its five lilac bushes flourished! White, purple, mauve.

Now, it could be that some of us, in season, when the nights were dark, might have surreptitiously climbed our back fences . . . But, of course, that can't be proved. All I know is, we all kept a sharp eye on those lilac bushes. A jealous eye.

Not infrequently, small boys of the neighbourhood would use the vacant and neglected garden for the Wild West playground for which it was ideally suited. But as soon as the lilacs were in bud, we made it a point to shoo them out. Indeed, as far as three back yards away, you might at this time of year hear distant voices calling, commanding boys to get the heck out of that. And not a little tension occasionally was generated over the telephones of the block when neighbour would call neighbour and firmly request the parents of small boys to call them away from the vacant house and its garden.

As one lady explained to me, across the back fence, in a low voice: "Really, it's more for fear they might get into mischief, breaking windows, and that sort of thing, that I telephoned her . . ."

But the neighbour who deserved most credit was Miss Thimblethwaite, a maiden lady, who lived next door to the vacant house. We could all see that she spent hours at her back windows, from about mid-April on. In fact, some of us, if we happened to be out for a breath of air in our gardens after dark, often had the impression that Miss Thimblethwaite was sitting in the darkness at one of her back windows, watching us.

Personally, I was very fond of Miss Thimblethwaite in a frustrated sort of way. She was the one person in the whole block with whom I was not on hearty, if perhaps false, terms of hiya, how's-everything neighbourliness. She was a spare little lady with a remote rather than a cold look for you, as you passed by. If she was sweeping off her front steps when I came by, she would just happen to have her back turned. If we met on the street, she would be just taking her hanky out of her purse as we passed. She obviously did not approve of me. Maybe she did not approve of cigarettes. Or the way I wore my hat. Miss Thimblethwaite was the kind of lady who likes gentlemen to wear their hats perfectly, vertically, on the tops of the middle of their heads. After five years, I wasn't even on silent hat-lifting terms with dear little prim Miss Thistlethwaite. I couldn't even catch her eye.

Well, sir, the lilacs were in bloom. You never saw such glory—white, purple, mauve. No lilacs bloom more lovely than neglected lilacs.

We would go into our gardens and potter about our poor little skimpy Persians and poke about at the last of the tulips and the oncoming perennials; but our eyes would turn and turn again. With the right breeze, a cloud of perfume would roll across . . .

It was 5.30 p.m. I came out the back door. To my horror, three small boys, crouched down in the weeds and last year's burdocks, half-hidden by thrusting themselves actually under the lower branches of the lilac bushes, were cautiously, delicately snapping off luscious gobs of the deepest, purplest flowers.

Tippy-toe, I went down the steps; and crouching, ran for the foot of my garden. I gathered my lungs full of wind in readiness.

Slowly, I raised my head over the fence.

"GET OUT OF THAT!" I roared, like a sergeant-major.

The three small boys froze, crouched.

"COME ON!" I bellowed. "I CAN SEE YOU SNEAK-ING IN THERE! GET OUT OF THAT BEFORE I CALL THE POLICE!!!"

That did it.

The three little fellows, dropping their bouquets, wriggled out of the secrecy of the purple lilac bush and, stooping low, ran like squirrels to the right.

And to the left, wriggling out of the secrecy of the white lilac bush, a little farther away, ran little crouched Miss Thimblethwaite, tossing away her assorted bundle of white and mauve as she ran, in abject terror.

And in abject terror, crouching, I turned and ran the length of my garden and up the steps and in the back door.

Did the little boys know Miss Thimblethwaite was there? I doubt it.

Did Miss Thimblethwaite know the little boys were there? I doubt it.

All I know is, I didn't know Miss Thimblethwaite was there.

But it would be hopeless to try to explain that to her.

Teleyawny

"QUITTING EARLY?" remarked Bert Jackson. He had been in the downtown bus line-up ahead of me, but dropped back to join me. It was about 4 p.m.

"I like to get away ahead of the five o'clock rush," I admitted.

"Man," said Bert, "this time of year sure gets me down." He opened his mouth in an enormous yawn.

"Aw," he heaved, "WAW!"

It was all I could do to stifle a yawn back at him. My cheeks ached with cramp in the effort.

Not that I mind Bert Jackson. It was just that having him here, going to sit beside me all the thirty-five minutes home on the bus, was not going to be as relaxed as if I were sitting alone, with my parcels on my lap, slouched down comfortably, half dozing. That was what I had had in mind.

But with Bert you can't do that. He is one of those fellows full of mental activity, curiosity, experiment. He would sit beside me all the way home briefing me on some weird and wild theory that had just occurred to him, and I wouldn't be able even to half-close my eyes.

"Yes, sir," said Bert, "this part of March is like four o'clock in the morning. It is four o'clock of the morning of the year. The deadest, ghastliest, ghostliest hour before dawn!"

The arrival of the bus interrupted his poetical kick.

By the time we climbed aboard, all seats were taken, so we selected hanging straps near the front, which is better than getting jammed in amidships in a bus where people butt you both coming and going. Up front, they just butt you coming.

— 39 —

What I had hoped for was one seat. I could offer it to Bert, and if he took it, that left me free to be butted on down the aisle. If I took it, I would be too low down for Bert to do much haranguing. But it wasn't to be. On straps, I was his audience.

"Just look," began Bert, as the bus took off, "at the faces in this bus! Did you ever see such exhaustion?"

I glanced down the congregation of the bus. They were a weary-looking bunch.

"People don't look like that," said Bert, "in November, or January, or August. It is only in March that we all get this fatigue."

At the word "fatigue," Bert opened his mouth wide again and launched himself on to another huge yawn.

"Aw," he went, with deep satisfaction, "WAW!"

I was looking at him, and felt my jaws stiffen, my cheeks ache.

"Let it go!" exclaimed Bert, seeing me. "Never hold a yawn in. It's not good for you."

So I opened my mouth. But it was by this time only half a yawn.

"Uff!" said I.

"Do you know something?" said Bert. "I could set this whole busload yawning in two minutes. The power of suggestion. It is a well-known fact in psychology.

"Sort of telepathy," I suggested.

"Teleyawny," corrected Bert. "Watch this, now."

He was hung on the strap facing back down the bus. I turned to face that way too.

"OOO," I heard him start, "Waw!"

Several sleepy faces were upturned. Three of them yawned almost instantly, in response to Bert.

He nudged me.

But the reason I then yawned was in response to the three whom I was facing.

"Yaw," I went. "Mmmmmm."

A man reading a newspaper looked up and saw me. As his gaze returned to his paper, he promptly emitted a large, loose, noisy yawn.

"Aw," said Bert behind me, "waw!"

The lady sitting next to the gentleman reading the paper raised her nose in the air, like a dog about to howl, and indulged in a good big fat yawn.

In less than two minutes, as Bert had foretold, the whole bus was yawning. And the harder they yawned, the more contagious it became. If I hadn't had to yawn I would have burst out laughing at the ludicrous spectacle.

"It's an epidemaw—WAW!" said Bert.

"It's hardly faw—waw," I protested, "hardly fair to play a trick like this on a bunch of people so tired . . ."

"It'll do them goooo—WAW!" disagreed Bert.

At which moment, a gentleman near the back of the bus got to his feet and struggled with the bus window by which he was sitting.

"Open your windows, everybody!" he shouted.

Everyone ceased yawning to turn and stare at him.

"Driver!" he yelled, as the bus drew toward a stop. "Driver, stop the bus and have all windows opened!"

"What's the matter?" someone called.

"The exhaust!" cried the gentleman, his head half out the window he had open. "Carbon monoxide!"

The driver now had the bus stopped and was standing up facing back.

"What goes on?" he inquired.

"Your exhaust!" shouted the gentleman. "Everybody is

yawning. Sure sign of carbon monoxide! Get the windows open! Vacate the bus."

"Aw, hold on!" said the driver. "There's nothing the matter with this exhaust. It was checked Monday."

He paused, looked at his passengers:

"Waw," he went, "hoooo!"

Half a dozen passengers had already risen to their feet and were moving with the quiet dexterity of the over-anxious to the exit door of the bus.

Others were hastily hoisting the windows beside them.

The raw March wind blew through the bus.

The bus driver shoved the lever that opens the rear door, and the six got off.

"O.K.?" he called, giving us a last look over his shoulder.

But we could all see, by the way his jaw bulged out, that he had got in a yawn even as he finished the word.

"Let's sit," said Bert.

We went back to one of the vacated seats.

"This is better," sighed Bert, sinking down.

"Waw," I agreed, "much baw-waw."

And for the remaining twenty minutes of our journey, Bert was content to look out the bus window and yawn, rather than transfix me with any new aspects of the month of March or angles on the power of suggestion.

The Terror

MRS. CHATTERLY (which, OF COURSE, is not her right name; I use it merely to protect the innocent) is the terror of our summer-cottage community.

She is a small, slight, energetic woman with several half-grown children who live in constant skedaddling, hustling fear of her tongue, which can reach right across our bay and around several islands.

She minces no words. She makes no bones. She calls a spade a spade. She stands for no nonsense.

No nonsense from her children, and no nonsense from anybody else, either, including all us neighbours. If we deserve a calling-down on any grounds whatever, Mrs. Chatterly takes it upon herself, as one properly qualified, to do the public duty. For instance, if we let the children go surfboard-riding in that period of an hour or two after lunch when a decent peace and quiet should prevail over the bay and all respectable people are resting after lunch, it is Mrs. Chatterly who gets her long-legged oldest son to row her across in their rowboat and, without preamble or any social fiddle-faddle, comes straight to the point.

"I speak," she says, "on behalf of the whole community."

Most of us doubt this. But it is foolish to try to debate with Mrs. Chatterly. She simply raises her voice, her small blue eyes grow round and gimletty, her words take on the staccato velocity and the deadly accuracy of a machine gun.

On quiet evenings, when the wind drops, it is, I must confess, one of the pleasures of our community is to sit on our verandas and listen across the water to the drama of the Chatterlys. Even with your eyes closed, you can pretty well visualize the whole performance. Chatterly (which is, as I say, not his right name, and if ever an innocent needed to be protected, Chatterly does) spends his two weeks at the cottage, and every weekend through the summer. He goes about with a small permanent hump of abasement at the back of his neck, and looks as if he had been stunned several years ago and had never quite recovered full consciousness. The time for the wind to drop is when Chatterly arrives on weekends and the long-legged boy rows him across from the Landing to their cottage. Mrs. Chatterly is on the wharf to greet him. And he always brings the wrong things. He is, of course, laden with provender from the city—much better stuff than the local store at the Landing provides. They are sheer robbers naturally.

But if he brings a leg of lamb, it was a roast of veal she told him, distinctly, to bring. If it's a basket of peaches, it was plums she told him, plums, plums, PLUMS.

In a way, we all hate to see poor Chatterly arrive; but we wouldn't miss it for worlds, and we all pray for a calm evening, when the acoustics are best.

However, it was Sam Brown—of all people, dear old Sam Brown, the general handyman, factotum and do-it-all of our community—who gave Mrs. Chatterly the devastating blow that has been piling up for her all these summers.

Sam lives at the Landing. It is he who puts the ice in our ice houses in winter, paints our verandas, repairs our roofs, keeps our outboard engines running. Sam is a gentle, middle-aged man who never learned to read or write, and therefore has to submit all his bills orally. I doubt if he has ever collected half of what is coming to him for the work he has done for us all. Most of us have to remind him of the things he did for us last May. He is an extremely handsome man, however ragged his clothes; and some of our wives are a little nettled over the fact that whenever distinguished-looking strangers arrive at the Landing, it is always to Sam they go, respectfully, for information, as if he were obviously the leading citizen of our community.

But we all love him, man, woman and child, and have a protective feeling about him that he cannot help but be aware of, and it must be nice for him to think of it, when he is in his little shanty up here at the Landing all the long winter through.

Thus, last Saturday, when Chatterly rowed his wife over to the wharf at the Landing to pick up their mail and newspaper, the crowd of us on the broad veranda of the general store-post office were a pretty unsympathetic audience for the Terror, when she got her eye on Sam.

He was in our midst, cheerily listening to all of us giving him the end-of-the-season suggestions of what we wanted him to do this fall and winter around our places. Mrs. Chatterly stamped brightly up the steps, poor Chatterly following humbly at her heels. When she saw Sam Brown, sitting on a box, with the twelve or fifteen of us draped happily around him, the light of battle lit in her eyes.

"Sam!" she yelped, cutting through all of us as if we had been fresh cheese, and striding to stand right in front of him. "You said you were coming over to test those propane tanks of ours!"

"Well, uh . . ." said Sam, rising from his box and removing his old cap.

"You also," said Mrs. Chatterly, glancing around the circle of us to indicate that what she was now about to do was in the public interest, and something that had needed to be done all summer long. "You also said you would look at the shingles on that back porch of ours."

"Well, uh . . ." said Sam.

"What's more," snapped Mrs. Chatterly, her voice taking on that added velocity with which we were all familiar, and which stiffens us with nameless fright, "you were going to build a diving raft for me. When was it? Let me see. It was about July 4 you said you were going to build us a diving raft."

Mrs. Chatterly again swivelled a glance around the company of us, a glance that accepted our undoubted approbation.

"Sam," she clinched, "I will have you understand that this community expects a man to keep his promises. We can't put up with . . ."

Sam waved his cap in front of Mrs. Chatterly's face.

He seemed to swell up. The gentle expression of his handsome weathered face tightened, his quizzical eyes began to glitter.

Mrs. Chatterly, thunderstruck by that cap waved in her face, fell back a pace.

"Mrs. Chatterly," said Sam Brown, distinctly, "I'd have you kindly not speak to me as if I wuz your husband!"

I imagine there never was such an instant of utter silence on the general-store veranda in all its sixty years.

My neighbour McBain started it. He tried to breathe in, and snorted instead. It was like a cork pulled. The veranda rocked with shouts, hoots and screams of laughter, the kind of laughter that has been stashed away and stored up for years, until it builds a kind of pressure. And we staggered over and gripped Sam's arms and shook them, and leaned on him, and hooted and howled, and slapped his back, until poor Sam was bewildered.

For the Reign of Terror was over. Mrs. Chatterly had, on quick feet, gone into the store, with Chatterly crowding close behind her.

But the story was spreading like a bush fire, some of us going down to the wharf to meet incoming boats, others of us even going into the store, with Mrs. Chatterly leaning right there over the counter, to regale whoever we could grab by the shirt front to express the glad tidings.

When the Chatterlys left, in a matter of five minutes, Chatterly was walking in front and, by the holy, the hump behind his neck was gone.

That was all a week ago.

There have been several calm nights.

Nobody has heard a peep from Chatterly's Point.

The Music Box

"YOU'RE IN LUCK!" announced my elderly friend Dandy Daniels when I picked up the phone.

"Luck?"

"I've got," cried old Dandy, "your music box!"

"Music box?"

"You told me," said Dandy, with sudden patience, "that if I ever saw a cute music box at any of these auction sales . . ."

"Aw, Dandy," I protested, "that was ten or fifteen years ago. That's when I lived in the big house. In this small house now, I'd have no . . ."

"You're reneging!" accused Dandy. "Here I went to all the trouble of going to this auction sale and bidding on this dear little music box. Rosewood, with inlays; and it plays the sweetest little old-fashioned tunes. Coming Through the Rye. The Waltz of the . . ."

"How much was it?" I checked.

Old Dandy, who is in his eighties, has a profound respect for money. He speaks of it with bated breath. He pauses before uttering such things as sums and amounts.

He paused.

"Twenty dollars," he said, reverently.

"Aw, Dandy," I said.

"Well, heck, I got it specially for you," cried Dandy, vehemently. "You asked me to keep my eye open. If I ever saw a cute little . . ."

There is no use arguing with old Dandy. A carnivorous old bachelor, he lives in his cosy small house with his housekeeper, Hortense, who has been with him over forty years. He has been collecting money by one means and another short of theft and highway robbery for over three-quarters of a century. He's got plenty.

Normally, I am the one who drives old Dandy out to the country looking for farm auction sales. Indeed, Dandy has outlived everybody who might ever have taken him for drives. And there were few of them, I imagine. But there is something about the old pirate that appeals to me.

He does not rely on me entirely. He and Hortense, for years past, have been preying on the real-estate profession.

Every once in a while, when they feel like going for a drive, they telephone a real-estate agent—and they keep a careful tabulation in the yellow pages of their telephone book, so as to approach a new real-estate agent each time—and tell him they are thinking of selling their neat small house and buying a larger one.

Naturally, the real-estate agent comes and inspects their house. And foreseeing a double deal, he then drives old Dandy and Hortense all over town. They have a whale of a time invading all manner of other people's homes, having a delightful time exploring private domiciles, poking and inspecting in living rooms, bedrooms, cellars, attics. They will keep the man four or five days, picking them up and driving them from district to district, and having a wonderful adventure seeing how other people live, intruding at all hours of the day into the homes of those desirous of selling. Naturally, while out in the agent's car, they do a little shopping in passing; and the agent often invites them in some place for a cup of coffee.

"Usually," says Dandy, "I have a sandwich too, while I'm at it."

Then, when they are satisfied and have had a nice outing, they inform the real-estate agent that they have seen nothing they fancy, and have decided to keep their old house.

Keep it? They wouldn't part with it for gold.

But how I came by this music box: Dandy and Hortense thought up the bright idea that they would exchange their city house for a nice farm.

And they got a real-estate dealer who deals in farm property. And he, after one look at Dandy's pretty little house, was willing to drive them all over the province in search of a good trade.

They had a whole week in the country.

"And naturally," confided old Dandy, when I arrived at his house to see my music box, "we came across a few auctions. The young punk the real-estate firm sent to drive us around the country was most respectful of my years, see? So I had no trouble having him stop at any auction sales we came across . . ."

"You got this," I asked, "at one of the auctions?"

I was frankly a little disappointed in my new music box. It was rosewood, true enough, and had inlays on the lid. But it was badly scarred and battered. Children must have had it for a plaything. I discovered, when Dandy wound it up and played it, that its tone was very thin and faint, and certainly some of the teeth were missing off the brass cylinder. You had to prop the playing lever in the "on" position with a chip of wood.

"It doesn't seem to be worth $20, Dandy," I suggested guardedly.

Dandy sat back and glared at me indignantly.

At this moment, Hortense came in the sitting-room.

"Wait," she said, seeing us with the music box, "until you see the other one."

Hortense is very deaf.

"HORTENSE!" shouted Dandy. "Get us a pot of tea!"

"Yes," said Hortense, retreating promptly.

"O.K.," declared Dandy hurriedly. "Hand over the twenty bucks."

"Now, just a second, Dandy," I temporized. "After all, this is a pretty beat-up little antique . . ."

Hortense appeared at the door, bearing in her arms a glossy, handsome object, as big as a suitcase.

"TEA!" shouted Dandy, trying to get to his feet. "TEA, I SAID!"

"O.K., O.K.," soothed Hortense, whom old Dandy has never really taken into his confidence in all the years they have lived together. "But take a look at this one. Rosewood, with these lovely inlays . . ."

"TEA!" yelled Dandy, attempting to shove the box away.

But Hortense pushed it on to the table before us, thrusting my poor little one aside.

"Twenty dollars," she exclaimed, "for the two!"

She lifted the lid, revealing a glass inner cover, and beautiful brass fixtures. She shoved the lever. Angelic music tinkled up.

I was sitting back, gazing levelly at old Dandy.

"She's deaf," he said, weakly. "Doesn't hear what's going on. Never gets the facts straight."

"Dandy!" I said.

"Paid a good deal more than $20 for this one," he said, patting it.

"Dandy!" I repeated, sadly.

"Aw, hell!" said Dandy, bitterly. "Women!"

So we sat until the tune ran out. It was one of Schubert's little airs. Hortense had gone to get the tea.

"Dandy," I said, when the sweet tinkle died, "I'll tell you what we'll do. I'll put up $10, and we'll toss. Whoever wins takes the good one."

"Nothing," stated Dandy, desperately, "doing!"

"Dandy! I'll put up $10, and we'll toss!"

"I don't believe in gambling," said Dandy.

I put two fives on the table, took a quarter from my pocket and tossed.

"Heads!" said Dandy hoarsely.

It was heads.

Dandy, with trembling old hand, reached and turned the lever for a new tune on the good one. It was After The Ball Is Over. He then picked up the two fives and stuffed them in his pocket.

"It coulda been worse," he exulted.

Straining

IT DOES NOT always pay you to revisit, with your old sweetie-pie, the scenes of your courtship. I did my courting, as you can see from my picture, in the days before night clubs or cozy cocktail bars or other hideaways. We did our courting in a tea room.

Tea rooms were the fashionable resorts of young people in the afternoons, after Varsity lectures were over, or after jobs were done at six P.M. For twenty-five cents each, you could get cinnamon toast and a pot of tea, cocoa or coffee. And in chintz-curtained gloom, either out in the main tea room or in one of the little side cubicles, you could idle away the hour. Tea rooms usually were one flight up, over gents' furnishings or cigar stores. They were presided over by very nice elderly ladies who wore little pinnies, and tiny lace caps pinned on top of their heads.

The other day, my wife and I were downtown in festive mood, walking along looking in all the bright store windows and feeling the stirring bump and push of the crowds, when I happened to look up. And there I saw, dangling in the late afternoon light, the sign of the tea room where, many a year ago, we had begun all this journey together.

"Look!" I cried, pointing.

"Let's!" cried my wife. "Why, I thought it was gone years ago!"

The store under it had gone, of course. Maybe a gents' furnishings, three shoe stores and a drug store had come and gone under it. But there it was, one flight up. We peered up the steep stairway. It looked a little steeper than we recollected.

Up we went, and you may believe it or not, but when we pushed open the curtained glass door at the top, who was sitting at the desk with the little black cash box in front of her, and with the same little lace cap, but one of the ladies who had waited on us long years before.

Recognition was mutual. This head lady insisted on waiting upon us herself, waving away the younger ladies, wearing little white pinnies and white lace caps, who stood ready in the chintzy gloom. There were not many customers for tea.

We chose the very cubicle we had known. It was little altered, though a little faded. We sat down, and I helped my wife off with her coat the same as I had done those years ago. I sat across from her, beaming the way I had once done. She ordered cinnamon toast and hot chocolate. I took tea.

It came, the head lady herself bringing it on the green tray with paper doilies. With a delicate gesture, she withdrew, drawing the curtains of the cubicle.

My wife poured her chocolate.

Something went plop.

We both leaned forward and peered down into her cup.

I am sorry to tell you this. It was three cockroaches.

Most regretfully, I went out and begged the head lady's indulgence. She came in and looked. She was stricken. She had to clutch the curtain for support.

"Mr. Clark," she said brokenly, "I don't know HOW this could have happened! We strain EVERYTHING in the kitchen!"

You see? It doesn't pay to revisit the scenes of your courtship.

The Just Man

CYRUS E. TOOHEY was sitting on the veranda of his summer cottage looking dreamily over the water, when a handsome cabin cruiser, all white, blue and varnish, drew abreast of him.

And a middle-aged man, with a sunburned bald head, wearing a white sweatshirt, appeared at the cruiser rail and dumped a large pail of garbage overside.

Now, Mr. Toohey is a just man. We all love and respect him. Apart entirely from the fact that he is worth a million if he is worth a nickel, we all love him. And before I tell you what action Mr. Toohey took, immediately, on seeing this outrageous action on the part of the sunburned bald-headed gentleman on the handsome cruiser, I would like time out for a minute to tell you about Mr. Toohey.

Oh, well, I will say that Mr. Toohey leaped to his feet, grabbed the binoculars that hang on the iron-woodpecker door knocker back of him, and trained them on the cruiser. He took its registered number off the bows, and its name off the stern.

And he wrote them down on the grey-painted veranda railing, in pencil.

"Hah!" said Mr. Toohey, hanging up the binoculars, and heading for his rowboat.

Well, now, about Mr. Toohey. His is the fourth cottage along the beach in our little summer community. It is a very plain little cottage. You would never take it for the summer home of a millionaire. What we like about Mr. Toohey is that he not only never exhibits his wealth in the material way, he never shows it in his social attitude toward us; the other eleven cottagers, eight of whom are salaried, and three of whom earn wages. He is as homely and gentle as the least of us. He brings fistfuls of wild flowers to the back doors, for the ladies. He helps paint. He helps shingle. If a wind builds up, he walks along the beach to see our boats are secure at the small wharfs, in case we are away. He'll hold a dog; which is the hardest part of getting porcupine quills out of them. But above all, he is a just man. He has no hates, no prejudices, no heat. It is a wonderful pleasure to go and sit on his veranda, or have him come and sit on ours, and listen to him on any subject whatsoever.

I saw him out in his rowboat, one hundred yards off shore, apparently picking things out of the water.

Mackenzie, another neighbour, and Mrs. Turnbull were down on the beach, watching. So I joined them.

"Some goon," said Mackenzie, "in a cabin cruiser, chucked a pailful of garbage overboard. It's going to drift in on the beach."

In a few minutes, Mr. Toohey rowed ashore.

In the boat he had some tin cans, half-orange skins, some soaked papers, a limp carton, three beer bottles . . .

"As near as I can figure," said Mr. Toohey, taking an old envelope from his pocket, "he dumped the following, though some may have sunk: three bean tins, two tomato tins, two peach tins, three beer bottles, eight half-orange skins, six soiled paper napkins, one carton, one paper box that had contained potato chips, one ketchup bottle, and a wad of newspaper containing coffee grounds, apple parings, grease, and the remains of several scraped plates."

"So?" said Mrs. Turnbull.

"You are my witnesses," said Mr. Toohey.

And I thought he had a very unfamiliar expression on his face.

He looked hot.

He went up the beach to his cottage, and returned with a basket into which he placed all his flotsam, and carried it back to the cottage.

"Never saw him mad before," said Mackenzie.

"Oof," said Mrs. Turnbull.

Monday noon, back in the city after the weekend, I was called on the phone by Mr. Toohey.

"Well," I cried, "and what are you doing back in town?"

Mr. Toohey spends the whole summer at the beach.

"Would you come to my office Wednesday, around 3:30?" asked Mr. Toohey.

"Certainly," I said, for none of us had ever been in a millionaire's office.

Wednesday, Mackenzie was already in Mr. Toohey's office when I arrived. It was very plain.

"From the Department of Transport, in Ottawa," said Mr. Toohey, "I have obtained the name of the owner of the cabin cruiser whose number and name I took last weekend. Hmmm? Maisie, my secretary, who knows the newspaper girls, got me a picture of the gentleman, from the newspaper files. He is the bald-headed, sunburned gentleman who dumped the pail of garbage. Without any doubt."

"Harrrumph," said Mackenzie.

"Ah," said I.

"Maisie has been clever enough," said Mr. Toohey, "to obtain, also through the society department of the newspaper, the news that the gentleman is entertaining, with his wife, a small select party to tea and cocktails at his city residence. The society editor was kind enough to say that the occasion is to be prettily celebrated on the side lawn of the residence. At 5 P.M. today, Wednesday."

Mr. Toohey touched a button.

Maisie appeared.

"Have you the basket? And the carton?" asked Mr. Toohey, gently. "Good and wet?"

Maisie returned with a basket full of tin cans, beer bottles, limp muck that doubtless had been paper napkins, cartons, paper boxes.

"Good," said Mr. Toohey.

Maisie then brought in tea and cookies.

At 4:30 we picked up the basket and the shapeless carton and other debris, which was in a plastic shopping bag.

Mr. Toohey drove to the rendezvous. It was in a very choice neighbourhood.

The side drive was full of cars, so we had to park in front.

"Come along," said Mr. Toohey, the just man. "You are my witnesses."

There were about thirty people on the side lawn around the bright metal tables and under the striped garden umbrellas.

The bald-headed man, beaming, came to greet us.

Mr. Toohey, with a wide fling, flung the contents of the basket across the lawn—bottles, cans. He took the shopping bag from Mackenzie, the dank carton from me, and gave them a royal hoist through the air.

The silence was paralyzing.

"What in hell . . . !" shouted the bald-headed man, very sunburned.

"If you examine that material closely," said Mr. Toohey, "you will discern that it is exactly what you chucked overboard from your cabin cruiser last Saturday afternoon, at about 4 P.M., in front of our summer homes."

He turned.

We turned.

We walked out to the car.

"Ha!" said Mr. Toohey, with immense satisfaction.

The Puff-ball

"HOW ABOUT a puff-ball?" said Skipper Howard over the long-distance telephone.

"How about it?" I cried, delighted.

For Skipper's farm, about forty-two miles from town, gives birth, every few years, to a wonderful crop of puff-balls. Some of them are as big as footballs, and I have seen them as big as Hallowe'en pumpkins.

"I've got my eye on one," said Skipper, "that will be ready in a day or two. A beauty. You know that pasture north of the house, with the slope up to the beech woods . . . ?"

"I'll be there!" I exulted. "Day after tomorrow."

"Bring your binoculars," said Skip.

"Oh?" I said. "What have you got?"

I meant birds. Skipper and I are both bird-watchers. We think wild birds, in their jewelled incredibility as seen through binoculars, are as perfect a representation of the joyous fantasy of the Creation as is to be found among living creatures. (I imagine that bird-watchers are people trying to come upon God unawares, to find Him not old, but forever young.)

"I'll show you when you get here," said Skipper slyly.

All the way up to Skipper's, two days later, I fricasseed in thoughts of puff-ball in butter. There are various ways of preparing this most delectable of all the fungi; but the one my Grandma showed me sixty (so help me) years ago, is simply fried in sweet butter. There are many myths about mushrooms. The ancient Greeks thought they were the food of gods. All I can say, to make myself perfectly clear, is that eating puff-ball is like standing in a familiar place and looking in a strange direction.

You turn on to a side road to get to Skip's farm, and after a few hills and valleys you find it sloping up to the right. I drove in the steep lane, and Skipper was standing on his side porch to greet me.

"How's my puff-ball?" I exclaimed, as we shook.

"Take a look," said Skipper.

I swept my gaze across the sloping pasture.

And there, half-way down to the road, was this magnificent white ball, big as a football, bigger, sitting in glory under the spare shade of a clump of bushes.

"My gosh, Skipper!" I cried in consternation. "It's in full view of the road!"

"Well?" said Skip.

"How have you protected it?" I demanded. "Everybody and his uncle passing . . ."

"Oh, I've protected it," assured Skipper. "Now, go on down, before somebody gets it, and pick it."

I had not taken my eyes off the beauty.

"I sure will," I breathed.

And off down the steps and through the fence and into the pasture I strode, joy mounting in every stride.

I could almost smell it cooking as I drew nearer. What a puff-ball! Perfect in its roundness. Glowing in its purity.

In fact, when I got within about twenty feet of it, the glow began to appear a trifle unearthly. And when I got within fifteen feet, my pace slackened. The last few paces I took with sinking heart.

For when I stood above it, I beheld that it was not a puff-ball at all. It was one of those darn frosted white globes that you see in the ceilings of kitchens and business offices, encasing the electric-light bulbs.

Four feet back of it, propped against a rock, was a sign lettered by Skipper. It read:

> This farm is private property.
> What are you doing on it?

I cannot begin to describe my feelings. I turned and looked back up the hill. There was Skipper, sitting on the side porch with his binoculars on me, enjoying my facial expression and rocking with laughter.

Slowly I climbed the hill.

"If you brought me up here . . ." I began.

"Don't worry, old boy!" hooted Skipper. "I brought you up here for two things. Don't worry. I've got your puffball safe and sound. It's back over by the wood lot. I was out to see it this morning. It's just coming into prime, twice as big as a football, solid and fresh . . ."

"Aaaaah!" I relaxed.

"But the reason I told you to bring your binoculars," said Skip, "I've had more fun, the past three or four days, with that light fixture down there. Every other car that passes on the road slews to a stop. They come creeping up the far side of the fence and climb cautiously over and run to the globe. Then they see and read the sign. I'm sitting here with my glasses. You should see their faces."

I went and got my binoculars from the car, and Skipper and I sat down in the rockers on the side porch for the fun.

We had not long to wait. The third car that came along slewed, just as Skipper had said, to a stop. Out jumped a man and a woman. They surveyed the hill. They studied the farm. Skipper and I sat still as mice. Then up along the far side of the fence the two climbed, crouching; and when they came level with the frosted globe, the man bellied slyly over the fence and, scrunched down, sped toward it. There he halted, stricken. You could see him wilting as he read the sign. He turned his astonished face up to us.

"Hoo-eeeee!" shouted Skip.

The man ran and vaulted the fence, and he and his lady scampered down the hill and into the car and away.

"Been going on," gasped Skipper, purple with laughter, "for three days! Haven't had so much fun in forty years."

"You'd think," I said, "they would smash the globe."

"They do," sighed Skipper. "But I got a dozen of them at one of those house-wrecking yards in town, for a buck. They've smashed three. But it's worth it. How about a pot of tea, and then we'll go back and collect the real McCoy?"

So we had a pot of tea; and as each minute passed, I reflected that it was but adding size and beauty to the magical growth of my treasure. And after the third cup, Skipper and I heaved to our feet and went out back and up the hill pasture to the wood lot.

"Prepare thyself!" said Skip, slackening his pace.

We came around a corner of the wood lot.

"It's gone!" he gasped.

We went forward. Skipper stared this way and that.

On a small shrub, impaled on a cut twig, fluttered a piece of paper.

Skipper picked it off. Its scrawl read:

"Sorry, old boy! To the true mycologist, property, in the sense of vulgar real estate, is without significance. Thank you."

"What," asked Skipper, "is a mycologist?"

"I am a mycologist," I replied abjectly. "It means one interested in fungi."

So Skipper has promised, though the season be late, that he will watch for another puff-ball. And when he finds it, he will first pick it, and THEN send for me.

The Walker

THERE ARE THOSE who would say that because I love to wander the midnight streets of foreign cities, I am in search of romance. Fortunately, romance is one of the things I have never had to go hunting for.

Freud, in his tidy, nosy, snuffly way, would have a fine time explaining how I got lost in behind Covent Garden, London, at 3 a.m. But of course Freud never read Charles Lamb when he was a boy, nor ever fell in love with a bygone city and a bygone age. By golly, has anybody made any inquiry as to what Freud was doing as a boy in Vienna? I'll bet it was something pretty peeky.

Certainly he didn't read the Essays of Elia, nor Mr. Pepys. Even if they did have translations of Dickens in Vienna in the eighteen-seventies, you can't actually translate Dickens. How, for instance, would you translate Mrs. Gummidge into ANY other language?

The theatre got out at 11.10 p.m. and Shaftesbury Avenue was packed with the theatre crowds all pushing toward Piccadilly. I refer, of course, to the first war.

But it occurred to me, looking at them, that the most interesting people were heading the opposite direction, toward Oxford Street, Holborn and Bloomsbury. So I joined them.

London is much the same at night in peace or war. I must admit that in the last war, the theatres went in at 6 p.m. and got out before 9, so as to let the crowds get home, or at least on the way home, before dark, when the bombers began to arrive. But the pubs keep the same pace, war or peace.

The crowd I was with streamed along, thinning into pubs, subway stations, buses, taxis, and by the time I reached

New Oxford Street and turned eastward toward Holborn, heading toward what they call The City, the quiet night was closing down. The pubs had closed. South of me, I knew, down any of the web of little streets, was Fleet Street. But if I kept on through Holborn Viaduct to Newgate Street, I would come to St. Paul's.

And if I came late enough, and thoughtfully enough, just wandering along, pretending I did not know where I was, and looking curiously into windows of dim small shops by the light of the street lamps, then, ignoring any chance passers-by who might be trying to share the night and mystery with me, I would happen, just happen, to look up.

And there, in the night sky, magical, would be the dome of St. Paul's, and not another soul on earth sharing it with me and Charles Lamb.

Aw, you know the feeling. It must have happened to you.

> "Some enchanted evening
> You may see a stranger
> Across a crowded room . . ."

Or, as a boy, when you saw a mountain for the first true time, or even a great hill, at a certain moment of beauty or a certain hour of waking tenderness in your young life.

Belated taxis, square and sputtery, were hastening past. Across the street, a few elderly Londoners were engaged in the darkness of some alley or lane, in loud, hot, beery argument. Strange that it is seldom the young in London who get into midnight fisticuffs. Always the elderly.

I crossed Newgate Street and turned left, instead of right, with the purpose of going north a block or two, through narrow deserted streets I had never been up before, so as to come back down toward St. Paul's from a new and more cherishable angle.

The street I chose was warehouses. Up from cellar-ways

came dank mouldy odors. I peered between the slats of locked yard gates, and all manner of merchandise could be imagined there in crates and tuns, though none was visible. Cats, the countless cats of London, came and walked with me. A night watchman turned his flashlight on me and seeing my uniform asked:

"Lost, sir?"

"No, no," I assured him heartily.

But I was.

The street I was on bent left. I took the next narrow street to the right. It was blacker than a hole, its street lamps so few I hurried from one to the next, and slowed as I reached it. I looked up at the street name, a board fastened to a rough brick wall. But what use are the names of streets that Charles Lamb never mentioned? No taxis came into these silent mazes. I could not even hear the far drone of buses. It was 1 a.m.

If I turned south, now, I would come out to Newgate Street, or Cheapside. I must. But which was south? My legs were tired. I began to hanker for my room in the Strand Palace Hotel.

I put on a little speed; my army heels smacked on the pavement. The street lamps grew dimmer, farther apart. The streets grew narrower, the musty sour smells creeping up areaways became stronger. No shop windows any more, but just the dim grey shapes of warehouses, small factories, aged, decrepit. At intersections, I would pause to listen for buses a block or two distant. None. If I waited a few moments, I might hear the tugs on the Thames hooting. It was 2 a.m.

Maybe I had been wrong in thinking south was this way. I tried a new way. I stepped faster. I watched for watchmen. I searched for a dim lit window. I went down two short narrow blocks and turned left. Far down, five blocks away, I saw a taxi whiz by.

What a relief! Those five blocks I walked with mount-ing assurance. I would forego St. Paul's tonight, and tell the driver to take me straight to the Strand Palace.

I came out on a broad dark street with handsome modern buildings on it.

"London" I said, being a stranger.

A taxi clattered near.

"Hoy!" I shouted, waving my stick.

"Full up!" came a voice passing.

Another taxi rounded a bend.

"Hey!"

"Night-night!" said the driver as he whizzed past.

I decided to walk what I decided was west. For the sky, far off, was ruddy with the lights of civilization.

Within a couple of blocks appeared a cab rank!

There, in the silence and the darkness, stood a row of seven or eight taxis, their lights dimmed, their drivers lean-ing about or sitting at the wheels. I strode to them, halting at the first one.

I opened its door.

"Strand Palace Hotel," I said, with the easiness of the true Londoner.

"STRAND Palace?" said the elderly driver. "You mean the REGENT Palace, don't you, guv'nor?"

"STRAND Palace, I said!" I repeated with the factuality my uniform and my rank entitled me to. And I got in and slammed the taxi door, relaxed, secure.

"Right-O!" sang out the elderly driver, shoving over his meter flag.

We started with a wide turn. We pulled up exactly across the street from where we started.

" 'Ere we are, sir!" sang out the cabbie, reaching through to open the door for me. "Shortest run I've 'ad tonight!"

Joe

DURING THE WAR, I was passing through Ottawa with a few hours to spare and decided to drop in and see my brother Joe, who was a Big Shot, as far as my profession was concerned. He was director of public relations for all three armed services—navy, army and air force.

His offices were on the street level of a building on Elgin street, across the park from the Chateau; and as I toddled up the street, looking for the building, which I had never visited before, I glanced in a large window and saw my brother Joe at his desk, bent over his work.

I stood watching him with brotherly affection. I hadn't seen the guy for two years or more, having been overseas as a war correspondent. Joe was my boss. He issued us war correspondents our licences, after having satisfied himself, through the R.C.M.P., the F.B.I. and Scotland Yard, that we weren't subversive characters or enemy agents.

For a moment, I thought of tapping on the window with my walking stick. It would be a nice, cock-eyed, family sort of thing to do. A surprise. But at that moment, a couple of generals came striding down Elgin street, and they gave me that cold-brass eye employed in war time for frowsy-looking civilians caught peering in the windows of official buildings.

Hastily, I went up to the entrance and entered.

Inside, all was hustle and bustle, soldiers, sailors and airmen of many ranks buzzing about. I followed along to what I figured was the entrance to Joe's office. A corporal was sitting at a little table just inside the door.

"Sir?"

"I'd like to see Mr. Clark."

"Fill this out, please."

He slid a mimeographed slip, with space for name, nature of business and so on.

"I'd rather not give my name," I said, sliding the slip back to the corporal. "And my business is strictly personal."

The corporal stood up.

"Mr. Clark," he said, "is very busy. If you have no appointment, you have to state your name, the nature of your business and so on. Fill this out."

"Look," I said, firmly. "I'm a citizen of this country. Mr. Clark is a public servant, is he not? I have a right to see him on private and personal matters that I don't figure I should have to submit to every Tom, Dick and corporal."

The corporal gave a bitter smile around, and nobody was listening. But you could guess a certain number of cranks were in the habit of trying to see my brother Joe.

"Fill this out," he said, patiently sliding the slip to me.

"May I see Mr. Clark's secretary?" I demanded hotly.

The corporal strode over and spoke in the ear of a young lady. She looked up and studied me with distaste. With a sigh, she got up and accompanied the corporal back to the desk.

"What do you want to see Mr. Clark about?" she asked.

"It's strictly," I declared, "personal. Look here: I'm a citizen of this country. Mr. Clark is a public servant, isn't he? Or am I wrong? Have I no rights? . . ."

The secretary eyed me carefully. She eyed my battered hat. She ran her eyes over my old, foxy face, the face of a fanatic if ever she saw one. She detected hostility, or even lunacy, in my eyes. She eyed my muffler, my loud overcoat, my walking stick, my large boots. A nut, she figured, for sure.

"Mr. Clark is too busy today," she said, "to see anyone."

"Very good," I said, in deep indignation.

And with outrage in my back, I stamped out.

I got out on to Elgin street and hurried to the window. I peeped in, and Joe was still bent over his desk, no one else in the room. I tapped.

Joe glanced up, surprised. Then he waved joyously, signalling me to come around in. I wagged my head urgently and signalled him to come to the window. It was one of those tall windows that open out from the middle. Joe opened, and we clasped hands.

"Come on around!" he cried.

"No, no, let me in here," I hastened. "Here, give me a hoist."

Over the window sill I went. I explained to Joe about the corporal and the secretary.

"Hurroo!" exulted Joe, dancing. "Take your coat off!"

As soon as I was comfortably seated, Joe picked up the phone. Sternly he asked the secretary to get the corporal and come right in with him.

In a moment, they entered.

With horror, they halted, staring at me. Over the corporal's face spread a sly, delighted grin. He pulled himself together for the pleasuring of bouncing me right out on my ear.

"Miss So-and-So," said Joe, "Corporal, I'd like you to meet my brother."

Their mouths opened.

"How," said the corporal, weakly, "how the hell did you get in here?"

Joe and I pointed to the window.

When I left, it was by the door, and Joe accompanied me past the corporal, for security.

"Sir," said the corporal to Joe as I was leaving, "would you give me a list of your brothers? With descriptions?"

Disclosure

TO US old soldiers, these westerns on TV are a laugh. It is the pistol-shooting that kills us. Those marshalls and deputies, those badmen, stalking with stiff legs held slightly apart, like little boys with wet diapers, and—wham!—the badmen are dead in the dust. Never a quiver. Clunk. Dead.

Right through the heart they get one another. Never a miss. Nobody is ever hit in the foot, or has an ear clipped, like in real-life shooting.

We old soldiers know. Thousands upon thousands of us who were officers carried revolvers to distinguish us from the rifle-carrying private soldiers. It was, you might say, a rank badge. If you couldn't tell an officer at a little distance either by his rank badges on his shoulders or by his bossy behaviour, the revolver on his belt identified him.

But shooting? Listen, chum. I bet 98 per cent of them couldn't have hit a barrel of apples at thirty feet, the distance these gun-slingers and marshals face each other. Confidentially, between you and me, except on rare occasions, most of us just had the holster on our belts. No revolvers in them. A Colt or Smith & Wesson .45 weighed around three pounds, and a British Webley even more. So, as a rule, after an officer had seen a couple of months' active service, he usually stuffed a pair of socks in his pistol holster.

My first pistol was a big black Colt automatic .45 that weighed about three pounds. And as I weighed only 106 pounds at the time, this caused a decided list to port when I dressed for parade. To keep the regulation three paces in front of my platoon, when I was fully armed, necessitated that I lope rather than march. So it was generally agreed among my platoon that the first German Luger pistol that came our way should be sold to me at a reasonable price. In one of our early skirmishes, a Luger, weighing half as much as the .45s, was shortly on my belt. Thus, when we were out of the line and doing training such as musketry on makeshift rifle ranges behind some French village, and while the troops were banging away showing themselves what bad shots they were, we officers were around behind the barn discovering how hard it is to hit a barn door with a pistol.

Of course, in battle, a pistol has its uses as a morale-booster. When an officer felt his morale slipping, he could draw forth his gat and blast off three or four rounds to add to the general dim. And this gave him a sense of participation. Togetherness we call it, today.

There are, of course, in every officer's memory, exceptions to this generality about pistols. And as I sit now watching a TV western, silently deriding all this fancy shooting by marshall or villain, there drifts into my mind the time I calmly drew forth my new Luger with the nine-inch barrel, and, in front of 200 derisive men, took aim . . .

No, no. Nobody was killed. It isn't a romantic story. All I hit was an empty rum jar. But it was a masterpiece of marksmanship, and I have treasured the memory of it for forty-two years, until just this week.

Having outlived everybody else, I was now a major. And there, in the misty twilight of a late September evening, I was leading my company of four platoons and four lieutenants across the battered fields of France toward Bourlon Wood.

On the march into the line, you halt five minutes at the

half hour, and ten minutes at the hour. Your men fall out on to the road banks, unsling their rifles and lie back to rest, leaning on their heavy packs. Relaxed they indulge in such witticisms as soldiers come by. And as I, their major, as was my habit, walked back among them to regard them with a fatherly air and exchange the odd witticism with the old-timers among them, I was subjected to rather more snorts, snickers, muttered inaudibilities and bursts of coarse laughter than usual.

Because on my belt and down my leg I wore a new Luger that Pte. George Bertrand, my batman, had secured for me in honour of our having become a major. (Batmen partake of the fortunes of their officers. Bertrand and I had become a major, you understand.) So he had traded my old short Luger and 150 francs for this magnificent German Navy model Luger, a nine-inch barrel, with the batman of an Army Service Corps colonel. (Batmen carried on this sort of commerce as part of their racket.)

Anyway, in its beautiful mahogany-red leather case, this weapon, suspended from my belt, was the subject of considerable hilarity among my troops reclining there in the twilight on the banks of the French mud road. There were ribald references to howitzers, Big Berthas, Brown Besses, artillery, grapeshot and the Battle of Waterloo.

As I retraced my steps toward the head of the column, preparatory to giving the command to fall in and continue the march to Bourlon Wood, I noticed one of those piles of salvage that the Salvage Corps used to gather up off the battlefield—broken rifles, tin hats, equipment, junk. And on the top of this pile, about 25 yards back off the roadway, some joker had placed an empty rum jar.

I halted. I gazed across across the intervening space.

Slowly, I began to unbuckle the holster of my magnificent Luger.

Up and down the recumbent straggle of my men, silence fell. They nudged one another. They craned around.

I charged the Luger, clack. I raised it calmly and took slow, steady aim.

Ker-ack! Bam!

The rum jar flew into a hundred pieces.

Cheers burst from my trusty men. Some of them scrambled to their feet to congratulate me.

"Tut-tut, men," said I. "It is nothing."

And, while I never again fired another shot from that pistol, for fear of destroying a beautiful moment in my life, I walked with a new assurance, I can tell you. And I could tell by their cheery and humourous faces that my men were much impressed. For weeks after, they would often mention it to me.

That is the memory I have cherished all these forty-two years. Since I have been watching westerns the last couple of years, it is a memory that has come back oftener, and with growing clarity.

Until the beginning of the week, when my old comrade, Sgt. Bud Hogan, blew into town from the north country, and put his feet on my desk and we sailed away across the years to dwell in reminiscence for a while in the olden times when we were young.

"Do you remember," said Hogan, "the time we was on the march up to Bourlon Wood, and you was carrying that great big German gat on your belt?"

"Ah, yes, yes," said I, "I remember it well."

"The boys got a wonderful kick out of that," said Hogan.

"I'm sure they did," said I. "And so did I."

"How long was it," asked Hogan, "before you found out about it?"

"How do you mean?" I asked.

"Well, about me hitting it," said Hogan.

My heart froze. "YOU hitting it?" I said.

"You don't mean to tell me," snorted Hogan, "that you STILL think you hit it?"

But he could tell by my face that I did.

"Hell," said Hogan, "I happened to see you staring at that salvage pile. And I noticed you starting to unbuckle your gat. The way the boys was ragging you, I suddenly got the hunch you was going to take a shot at that rum jar. I was back of you, so I nipped to my feet, jacked a shell into my rifle. And when you fired, I fired."

"But how do you know," I demanded, brokenly, "that it was you . . .?"

"Aw, Major!" protested Hogan, with a laugh. "It was a good twenty-five yards. The boys enjoyed it immensely. We passed the word all through the company for nobody to let on, because you were so proud. The way you walked off to the head of the column, and the way you sang out your commands . . . Aw, it was great! But I thought SURELY by this time you would have found out."

The last couple of westerns I've seen this week seem to have lost something.

I have the feeling that somebody with a rifle, off camera, is really doing the shooting, even though I know in my heart that those villains dead in the dust aren't really dead at all.

Johnny-on-the-spot

EVERY SUMMER COLONY, I suppose, has its Bill Anderson, like ours.

Bill knows all the answers. No matter what happens, good or bad, Bill is in the middle of it. If we have a bush fire around the resort, Bill takes charge. If a child has the toothache, Bill pulls the offending molar with ordinary pliers, thus saving a trip to town.

He's the master of ceremonies at the regatta. He tells us all where the best place is to fish. The women think the world of him. He is a big, handsome man, usually in shorts and bare feet, sunburned the colour of a walnut. We men aren't so keen on him. (We men and a couple of married spinsters in our colony. No summer resort is complete without a couple of married spinsters to back up the men in their opinions.)

Bill's children, small, obedient, cowed, talented kids, win most of the prizes at the regatta. And it is true the last bush fire that started on Jones's Point, the Lands and Forests men chased Bill away and made him get the hell off the point altogether, when they arrived to fight the fire. We men also like to remember that when Bill pulled the Herkimer boy's tooth, year before last, infection set in, and the Herkimers not only had to take the boy to town, they didn't come back for the rest of the summer.

None the less, Bill Anderson is Johnny-on-the-spot: and whenever anything untoward happens, everybody thinks of him first, or second.

Thus, when Joe Boyle saw a porcupine swimming across

to his island last week, his first thought was for his boxer, and his second was for Bill Anderson.

The Boyles' boxer is a large, tan, rubbery, wriggling dog whose face is split away back past his eyes, almost to his ears. His name is Buster. No dog in the world has to have as wide a gape as a boxer. And Buster is the gapingest boxer I ever saw. The mere thought of him being involved with a porcupine is enough to give Mother Nature herself the shivers.

Joe Boyle saw the porky, like an untidy bit of flotsam, high in the water, when it was about 100 yards off his island.

He started to yell for Buster, and the family all came bursting out of the cottage with screen doors slamming, at the frantic tone of Boyle's yells.

Even some of us neighbours came running to our verandas, to look across at the Boyles. We saw Joe and his wife and children furiously chasing Buster, who, boxer-like, was romping for all he was worth over the rocks and juniper bushes, and in and out of the groves. They finally caught Buster, and we watched them haul him into the boat house, and lock him up.

Then we saw Joe Boyle run to the wharf and jump into his outboard skiff. And we could hear Mrs. Boyle shouting to him to go straight and get Bill Anderson.

So naturally we figured something was amiss at the Boyles', and we got into our outboards and rowboats and canoes and proceeded to converge on their island.

"It's a porcupine!" Mrs. Boyle called to us, as we neighbours hove nigh. "Joe saw a porcupine swimming on to our island!"

Buster barked at us furiously and amiably from the cracks in the boat-house walls.

"Well, heck!" I said, for one. "Why don't we just go back and find it and club it on the head?"

"No, no!" cried Mrs. Boyle, and any other of our wives who had joined the congregation. "Wait for Bill Anderson!"

Bill, after all, has a .22 rifle.

"Aw, heck!" put in some of us other men. "We'll just walk back across the island and have a . . ."

"No, no, NO!" screamed the ladies. "Wait for Bill Anderson!"

So we waited; and in a few minutes, we perceived Joe Boyle coming full blast in his outboard, with Bill Anderson sitting alertly in the bow, with his .22 rifle at the ready.

"Hello, everybody!" said Bill, stepping athletically off the bow as the boat slid in. "Now, first, where's Buster?"

"Locked in the boat house."

"Good!" directed Bill, racking a cartridge into the rifle. "Now, everyone keep behind me. You men, we'll form a line to sweep the island. How long is it, Joe, since you first detected the porcupine?"

"Twenty minutes," hazarded Joe, rolling up his sleeves.

"Very good!" commanded Bill. "It will hardly have got off the island yet. Form line, men, and we will comb the island thoroughly, every bush, every tree, large and small. Keep your eyes peeled. The man who sees it first, shout for me. I'll be in the middle of the line. O.K. everybody? Form line!"

So we formed line, including a few of the more agile ladies, and we picked up sticks and cudgels, and began the sweep of Boyle's small island. We examined each clump of bush, we studied up every pine tree, we explored each gully and crevice, while Bill, commanding, shouted constant instructions to keep the line true.

And we got to the far end of the island without having detected the marauding beast.

"That's funny," said Bill, when we all assembled on the rear point of Boyle's island.

He scanned the distant waters shrewdly.

"Gentlemen," he said, "there is, after all, only one sensible thing to do. And that is, let Buster loose. It is the function of a dog to find game . . ."

"No, no, no," we all protested, horrified, thinking of that wide, homely, jovial maw on Buster, the one thing in the world that is, you might say, the antithesis, the counterpoint, the antipodes of porcupine.

"I," said Bill Anderson, grandly, "will, of course, have him on leash!"

"Well, of course . . ."

We all followed Bill back across the island. Buster was barking furiously from within the boat house at being debarred from all the excitement.

"Get me a stout rope," directed Bill, putting the safety catch on the .22.

Boyle got him a ten-foot piece of clothes line from the outside wall of the boat house.

"Open the door, carefully!" commanded Bill.

Boyle opened the door a crack.

Buster plunged into Anderson's waiting arms.

They wrestled.

"Steady, boy!" said Anderson, starting to arrange a loop around Buster's neck.

But Buster had other plans. He wriggled violently free, dived under the boat house; there was an agonized yelp, out came Buster, his wide face a blur of porcupine quills, while from the other side waddled a most indignant porky.

Anderson promptly shot the porky, while the rest of us chased Buster round and round as he madly fought the stinging barbs in his countenance.

There were seven of us when we finally got Buster wrapped in a quilt and all of us lying on top of him on the boat-house floor.

"Give me the pliers!" charged Anderson, reaching.

"You," said Boyle, the ingrate, "go and bury your porcupine."

Who's Where?

"HOW would you like," asked my sister Drew-Brook, "to give us some of Granddad's library?"

Thirty years ago, when I inherited my father's 2,000 books, the rest of the family were glad it was my responsibility to find sanctuary for them. You revere your father's books. You have to be a grandson to chuck them out.

But now the Drew-Brooks, realizing the dream of those who prosper in cities, had bought an old farm house and converted it into the most beautiful Homes & Gardens jewel box, thirty miles from town. And one of the rooms, my favourite, was a downstairs library with a log fireplace, and book shelves from floor to high, high ceiling.

"Why, certainly," I responded. "You bet. Of course. The collected works of Charles Dickens. The collected works, in twelve volumes, beautifully bound in ornate gilt-tooled bindings, of Benjamin Disraeli, Lord Beaconsfield, one-time Prime Minister of Britain and confidante of the late Queen Victoria."

"Good!" said my sister.

"Also," I ticked off, "the History of the Great War, in eight volumes . . ."

"Nothing doing," said her husband, Tommy.

"And," I enumerated, "the collected speeches of the Canadian Club, 1911 to 1937."

"Holy doodle!" said Tommy.

"Great Moments," I recounted, "in the World's History, in twelve volumes, magnificently bound in buckram, with gilt hand-tooled ornamentation."

"We'll take 'em," said my sister. "After all, we've got

to respect Dad's library. It will be our children who will throw them out."

So we went upstairs to my den, and into the upper hall, where I had built shelves for the overflow, and down cellar, and in remote cupboards, and got together a remarkable collection of books that I had long since forgotten I had.

As I hoked and poked, I came upon Who's Who for 1937. I remembered that there had been three of these at the time of my father's death, the British, the American and Canadian. Squat, fat, scarlet-bound volumes, they consisted of compact biographies, in fine type, of the contemporary notables in the economic and social life of their nation. I remember I gave the British and American to the high-school library. The Canadian I had kept. Nineteen thirty-seven.

"Ah!" I said, placing it on the Drew-Brook pile.

Tommy picked it off.

"For Pete's sake!" he exclaimed. "Nineteen thirty-seven!"

They would all be dead and gone by now, in that book. You don't get into Who's Who in any country until you are middle-aged or worse.

I took the book from Tommy and glanced through its close-typed pages. Not a name did I recognize. Where are the snows of yester-year? Who was Who? When? And for how long?

"Tom," I said, "there is one condition to this deal. You take this book."

"Aw," said Tom.

"I can't have you picking and choosing," I insisted. "After all, Great Moments in the World's History, in twelve volumes, bound in . . ."

"Awfff!" protested Tom.

"Will you take it?" I demanded. "And not chuck it out?"

"O.K.," submitted Tomy, slyly.

So in their station wagon, the Drew-Brooks took the half-ton of books that would help fill the lofty shelves in that cosy room with the log fireplace.

And it was the following spring, when my womenfolk were house-cleaning, and had all my books piled off their shelves, that I saw, to my astonishment, a some-what faded scarlet book, Who's Who. I picked it up. Nineteen thirty-seven.

"Where did this come from?" I inquired.

"It was in back of one of the shelves," said my ladies.

So the next time we went out to the Drew-Brook farm, I had Who's Who concealed under the raincoat over my arm. And shortly, while the rest of the menage were gossiping in the living room, I was, as usual in front of the log fire in the library. When it was safe, I climbed on a chair and stuck Who's Who, 1937, in between some other red-jacketed books on one of the topmost shelves.

And there, to my quiet satisfaction, I beheld it on my visits to the farm all through 1954.

But around Christmas that year, I was shaken to observe that it was gone.

I did not think it politic to inquire for it.

In March, 1955, my wife lost her cigarette lighter, and imagined it might has slipped down in behind the back seat of the car. I removed the cushion, and, in addition to the lighter, hair pins, gum wrappers and a few ball-point pens, I discovered a rather old red dusty book. Who's Who, 1937.

I dusted it off, took it indoors and had a happy time poring through all the famous men of an era already forgotten. Then, realizing it had been several weeks since we had visited the farm, we drove out through the snow.

On the shelf in Tommy's bedroom was a cardboard box

containing black ties to wear with tuxedos, elastic arm bands for holding dress-shirt cuffs just so, black silk socks, and such things a gentleman farmer needs, but not often. Maybe a couple of times a year.

I buried Who's Who, 1937, under all these appurtenances of fashion, and set the box carefully far back on the shelf.

In the summer of 1956, I was, if you will excuse the particulars, seated in our outdoor privy at our summer cottage on the Georgian Bay.

A spider was busy building its web, a big fat spider. And, like Robert Bruce in his cave, I sat and watched with interest. As it vanished into the upper gloom of the privy, my eye caught something peeping over the scantling. It was the corner of a book. Tingling with presentiment, I took the book down. Who's Who, 1937.

The Drew-Brooks also have a cottage on Georgian Bay, two miles from us. In the outboard, I paid them a visit. I was happy to meet them part way, all out sailing in their yawl.

On the top of their china cupboard in the cottage living room is a large rustic mantel clock. It does not go. It has not gone for years. Nobody ever looks at it. I placed Who's Who, 1937, behind the clock. I could not wholly conceal it. But I figured it would do.

Half way through the past summer, the Vinings were visiting the Drew-Brooks, Charles and Doris. At lunch, Charles glanced up.

"What's that book behind the clock?" he inquired.

"What!" cried Tommy.

"For heaven's sake!" screamed my sister.

So, while Charles thumbed through the book, thinking, no doubt, of the fragility of man, my sister and Tommy recounted in glee the ups and downs, the overs and backs, of this old book, and all the fun and determination involved.

Then Charles happened on the V's; and there he found, in a good four inches of space, the biography of his late father, Rev. Dr. A. J. Vining, with all his degrees and honours, and some account of his career as one of the greatest raisers of funds for the church. Charles did not know this record existed.

"May I," he asked, holding it up, "have this book?"

And so came to a happy end the whimsical journey of a book out of my father's library.

Favourites

AWAY LAST OCTOBER, Rory Cohen, who operates my favourite delicatessen store, pointed out his favourite customer to me.

When I entered the store there were half a dozen customers, and Rory was just coming out from the back, from behind the partition. And at sight of me, he gave me the signal.

He puts thumb and finger of his right hand together in the familiar O.K. sign, and gives a big fat wink. This means for me not to get waited on by either of the young ladies who help him, but to stand back and wait for him. It means he has got something special in behind the partition: some extra fine pickled herrings from Holland, or maybe some honey from Palestine, or a Danish cheese of superlative quality. And when my turns comes, he takes me in behind the partition. He does not expose these de luxe items to the general run of his customers.

As he gave me the signal, I noticed he had something done up in wax paper in his hand. And he carried it to a lady customer who was waiting at the counter.

I had never seen Rory so excessively polite as he was to this lady. He was fairly dancing with courtliness, as if he were a partner in a minuet. The lady took the parcel along with some others she had bought, and left. Rory eyes wide, signalled me to notice the lady as she went out the door. A middle-aged lady, quietly but smartly dressed, a lady, as Rory would say, of class.

Then he motioned me to follow him behind the partition.

"Well, well, WELL!" I said.

"She's my favourite customer!" exclaimed Rory. "I'm glad you saw her. My very favourite."

"I thought," I said, "I was your favourite customer."

"No, no," said Rory, still exalted. "You come up somewhere near the front. But she's SPECIAL."

"O.K., who is she?" I asked.

"I don't know!" cried Rory, "I don't even know her name! I just call her Mrs. Lovely."

"She's old enough to be your mother, Rory," I mentioned.

"It isn't THAT!" protested Rory indignantly. "She's just my favourite customer. She's a lady. She makes keeping a store a pleasure, if you know what I mean. She does something to the place, to the store, to me. She makes me feel . . . important!"

"Well, you are important," I cooled him. "What have you got here?"

It was a September cheese, 1957.

"I got it from down Woodstock," he said, impatiently "A September cheese! Prime Canadian Cheddar!"

And he snicked off a sliver for me to taste.

As usual with Rory's specials, it was good. It was superb. He let me have two pounds.

"Is this," I asked, "what you were sneaking out to your favourite lady?"

"Mrs. Lovely?" said Rory. "I let her have three pounds."

"How long has she been coming in?" I inquired.

Rory sat down on a box to relax and enjoy the memory.

"About four years," said Rory, looking very fey into space. "At first, I didn't notice her. But then I noticed she always stood back and let the pushers get ahead of her. She is shy. She just stood back, kinda blushing, with a look of embarrassment in her eyes. Eyes kinda wide. And one day, the idea came to me that she wasn't embarrassed for HER. She was embarrassed for them! The pushers. And suddenly, SUDDENLY, I knew I had a lady for a customer!"

Rory swayed back on the box.

"You get me?" he asked. "You get so sick, keeping a store, with all the greedy faces, the pushers, the sneaky ones. Maybe in your whole life you never see somebody who NEEDS you."

"Ah," said I.

"So right away," said Rory, "she became my favourite customer. And I been looking out for her, and watching for her, from day to day, week to week. She just comes in, now and then, picks up a few things and goes away. I don't even know where she LIVES!"

While I snicked off a couple more slivers of the September cheese, Rory leaned back, one knee cupped in his hands, thinking about Mrs. Lovely.

"I got a man like that, too," he said. "I call him Mr. Good. I found out his real name a year or so ago, Mac something. MacLean or MacLeod, or something; but I still call him Mr. Good, like I did after I first got on to him. He's been coming in five years or so. I guess you have seen him in here. He's got black bushy eyebrows and white hair. A gent. Somebody told me he was a lawyer."

"Does he," I asked, smacking the cheese, "come ahead of me among your more cherished customers?"

"Frankly, he does," said Rory. "He's another of those SPECIAL kind of people. No crowding. No hustle. He just waits his time, with a smile. And then he says: 'Well, Rory, what should I buy today?' Just like that."

"You should have a hundred customers like that," I agreed.

"He is interested," said Rory, "in what I got. But there is something extra. He is interested in ME."

"I get you," I said.

"A year ago Christmas," said Rory, "I was laid up. He gave the girls five cigars to bring me home. Five-for-a-dollar type cigars. With them, two English magazines all about food. I found out they were eighty cents apiece, those magazines!"

"Should I give you presents?" I asked.

"You miss the point!" cried Rory. "It's the WAY he acts. He makes me feel I am not a delicatessen store. He makes me feel I am professional! Man to man!"

I picked up my two-pound cut and Rory concealed it in wax paper for fear the outer customers might see it.

"Sometimes," said Rory, delaying me, "sometimes I dream the two of them will come into the store together. Mrs. Lovely and Mr. Good! And do you know what I will do?"

I smiled at him.

"I will turn to Mr. Good," thrilled Rory, "and I will say 'Mr. Good, I would like to introduce you to my favourite customer.' And Mrs. Lovely will blush all up and try to sink back through the wall. And then I will say 'Mrs. Lovely, I have the pleasure to introduce to you my SECOND favourite customer!'"

I led out past the partition.

"What I mean," said Rory anxiously beside me, "what a pleasure to make people like that ACQUAINTED!"

But as Rory tied the brown paper round my package of cheese, he was subdued, feeling I had not been with him all the way.

This morning, I went into Rory Cohen's.

The place was jumping. Rory had gone next door, to the

Italian fruit store, and got two or three dozen daffodils, and they were in jars on the counter and up on the shelf corners. His girls were tiptoe. There was a gala air about the store.

And when Rory saw me entering, he threw his arms over his head.

"Mr. Clark! Mr. Clark!" he shouted. "They came in together!"

"Who?" I asked.

"They came in together!" he cried, rushing around the end of the counter to me and shaking my lapels. "Mrs. Lovely and Mr. Good!"

"Good," said I.

"They been married together for THIRTY YEARS!" he exulted.

The Fire

NED'S News Stande & Smoke Shoppe is just a hole in the wall amid the topless towers of the downtown. But it is a pleasant hole to go into, out of the hurly-burly, cosy with its stacks of newspapers and magazines, fruitful like a library with its walls tiered to the ceiling with the merchandise of tobacco in all its shapes.

Ned is a philosopher, though quite a small one.

"Dismal weather, isn't it, Ned?" say I.

"It could be worse," says Ned.

A philosopher is one who has the same point of view as you, but is not upset by it.

I bought my weekend paper and my Sunday's supply of cigarettes, and then leaned my elbow on the only available space on the counter to exchange a few generalities with Ned.

The cigarette I was smoking was down to the butt. I turned to flip it out the doorway on to the pavement outside, and awaited a gap in the passing parade of legs.

I flipped.

"Good heavens!" I exclaimed.

"What is it?" asked Ned.

"I flipped my cigarette butt," I cried, "right into the cuff of that fellow's trousers!"

"What fellow?" inquired Ned.

"The one who stepped past the door," I gasped, "just as I let her fly."

"Don't worry," said Ned. "It couldn't go in."

"But it DID go in!" I protested. "I saw it."

"Pants cuffs," soothed Ned, "don't gape."

"But this one did," I said with urgency. "I saw it. The butt just went flip, right in it!"

"Then," said Ned, "what are you standing there for?"

"Of course!" I shouted. "What am I thinking of? Here, watch these. Don't let anybody . . ."

And I shoved my paper and packs of cigarettes to one side and bounded out the door.

As I manoeuvred up the street amidst the two-way throngs of pedestrians, it seemed to me the man with the cigarette butt in his trouser cuff had been wearing a dirty old trench coat. I couldn't be sure. But that was my hasty impression. I angled over to the curb side of the pavement to make time, and by craning as high as I could, I saw a man in a dirty trench coat standing at the intersection fifty yards ahead, waiting for the lights to turn.

I made haste.

But the lights turned and my man was lost in the bevy of pedestrians crossing.

I scuttled across the intersection.

Half way across, a strong hand seized me by the shoulder.

"Greg!" said the strong man.

"Joe!" I cried. "Joe Morgan! Look, Joe . . ."

"I haven't seen you in a dog's age," said Joe, holding to my lapel and fastening me there in the middle of the intersection with everybody passing hurriedly both ways.

"Joe, look, I flipped a cigarette butt into a guy's pant cuff . . ." I sputtered.

"Hold on, hold on," soothed Joe, trying to turn me and lead me back to the corner I had just left. "I haven't laid eyes on you for . . ."

"Joe, look, I . . ." I whimpered, wrenching myself free just as the lights changed.

I dashed for the far side.

Which way had the man in the dirty trench coat gone?

Straight on up? Or to the right or to the left? The home-going crowds were boiling this way and that at the intersection. It was impossible to see ahead in any direction.

This called for psychic powers. I decided on straight ahead. And again taking the outer curb, so that I could drop down on to the edge of the road to make time, I soon detected, quite far ahead, a figure in a dirty trench coat.

I was happy to note, as far as I could see, that no smoke was coming from his pant leg.

"Hey! Mr. Clark!" came a voice from a store doorway.

It was the optician, an old friend.

"I'll be back in a . . ." I called over my shoulder.

"Hold on," hallooed the optician. "That story the week before . . ."

But I held desperately to my course, though by taking my eyes off my quarry for only that instant, I had lost him. I dropped out on to the roadway and trotted.

He had vanished.

I stepped back up to the pavement and relaxed my pace to match that of the crowd.

"What a stupid thing!" I muttered.

A lady with whom I was in step gave me a sharp look and dropped back a pace.

It was at that instant I saw my man in the dirty trench coat standing in a shoe-store doorway, bent over and beating the cuff of his trousers with a folded-up newspaper.

I dashed to his rescue.

"It was a cigarette butt," I explained, when he glanced up at me.

"A what?" he asked.

Smoke was certainly coming from the smouldering cuff.

"I'm guilty," I informed him firmly. "I flipped a cigarette

butt out a doorway down the other block, and I saw it go right into your pant cuff."

Between us, we squeezed and smothered and squashed the smudge out. There was a hole in the back of the pant leg about the size of an orange.

"I've been chasing you," I puffed.

He stood up, smiled broadly at me and held out his hand.

"I've been trying," he said, "for two winters now to get rid of this damn' suit. But my wife says it's still good."

"But . . . but . . ." I expostulated. "It's my . . . I'm . . ."

"Do you know," demanded the man in the dirty trench coat, "how much she spends on one permanent?"

I shook my head.

"Fifteen bucks!" shouted my man.

"I'm responsible," I insisted. "I'll pay for the new pants."

"Not on your life," said he. "I've been trying to get rid of this."

So we shook hands again and parted. On the way back down to Ned's, the optician had gone. Joe Morgan wasn't to be seen on any of the four corners of the intersection.

"Well," asked Ned, "did you catch him?"

"Yes," I said. "But you'd never believe what happened."

"Not from you I wouldn't," agreed Ned, handing me my paper and my cigarettes.

The Navigator

"WE'LL GO by the Canthook Channel," said Ted Jenkins.

"Whoa," I said, "isn't that a pretty tricky route?"

We were in Ted Jenkin's new speed boat, a 22-footer.

He gave me that thin-lipped nautical smile of the true navigator.

"It's all marked," said he. "Anybody can follow it."

"By golly," I submitted, "the last time I was through there, I was in my outboard skiff. And I tell you it was pretty ticklish . . ."

"It's all thoroughly marked," said Ted, throttling open, and the little 22-footer surged up onto the waves and fairly floated ahead.

"Have you done it often?" I called across the deep snore of the engine.

"Never been in it," replied Ted, "but I had a look at the chart before we left. Here. Take a look."

He handed me the large, stiff chart rolled up.

I held it down out of the breeze on my lap and unrolled it part way.

"There," said Ted. "Look over on the left-hand side, see?"

I certainly could not see. All there was were some thin quavery lines, with numbers printed all over the open spaces.

"Look there a couple of inches from your thumb. See? Canthook Channel."

"You mean," I asked, "these spidery lines are the land?"

"That's right," said Ted very easy.

I let the chart roll up again, which it wanted to do.

"If you had looked at the Canthook Channel," said Ted, "you would have seen little symbols. They show the spar buoy positions out in the entrance of the channel, and also the beacons on shore."

"Have they got it lit?" I asked in surprise.

"No, no," laughed Ted. "A beacon is a white-painted range mark on the shore. When we pick up the first spar buoy—that's a red-painted pole anchored in the water—we simply look for the beacon that's marked there on the chart, and simply steer for it."

I began to wish I had come fishing with somebody in a smaller boat. It was all of twenty years since I had last been up here through the Canthook Channel. It is a route that winds in behind rocky islands, shoals and cliffs. But at the far end of the channel are several bays with some of the best fishing to be had for miles around.

"The way I remember it," I called, "you had to snake through. I had to shut off my engine in a couple of places and paddle through . . ."

"Greg, lad," said Ted, "relax! You know nothing about navigation. It's as simple as reading a menu in a restaurant, when you know how."

I have a great respect, a sort of reverence, for these experts. When I see these young pilots of aircraft on the street, I am inclined to tip my hat to them. I think ship's officers are the noblest of men. I even get a little kick of humility when I see the engineer of a trans-Canada Diesel.

Men who know how. They're the stuff.

So I relaxed as we sped swift and racy across the great open bay before we turned in for the Canthook Channel, and the two islands, Big Canthook and Little Canthook, that guard its entrance.

Ted, who wears a yachting cap at the proper angle, tilted a little forward over his left eye like the late Admiral Beatty, was holding the wheel lightly. His eyes were half closed. He loves boats. This one we were in was his biggest so far. His dream is a cabin cruiser, forty-feet long.

"Can you pick up the red spar buoy?" he called cheerily, staring ahead.

All I could see were the distant rocks of Big Canthook.

"I've got it," he said. "You'll see it presently."

And sure enough, in about five minutes, I could detect the red pole slanting up out of the waves far ahead.

"Hadn't we better slow down a little?" I asked. For the shore was fast approaching.

Ted patted me on the top of the head and gave me another nautical smile.

"Open the chart, lad," he said, "so I can read it."

Hastily, I unrolled the chart and held it on my lap, leaning over so Ted could see it.

"See?" he said. "When you pass the red spar buoy, you pick up that beacon to the left, there. Got it?"

"Nope," said I.

We passed the red spar buoy full out.

Ted pointed. On the shore, a quarter mile away, was a triangular white object.

"Thar she lies!" said Ted, wheeling the boat to point straight at it.

It didn't look like a marker to me. It looked like a man in a white shirt with his hands on his hips.

"It looks to me," I called, "like a man in a white shirt and khaki pants, with his hands on his hips."

"Heh, heh!" called Ted.

It seems navigators should never say "Heh, heh!"

For hardly had Ted uttered it before we hit with a dull, sickening thud, as they used to say in Sherlock Holmes's time.

The boat humped up, slid sideways, clonked, clanked, the engine screamed, and Ted, his yachting cap over his nose, turned off the juice.

The beacon came running down the rocks.

"Are we going to sink?" I asked Ted, in the silence.

"I've probably," said Ted, hoarsely, "just bent my propeller shaft."

That is all we had done.

We drifted ashore; and the beacon, who sure enough was a man in khaki pants and a white shirt, was waiting to fend us off the rocks with his foot.

Ted was quite short with him.

"Thanks," he said stiffly, when the beacon caught a line thrown by Ted. Line, that's what you call it. Not rope.

So we scrambled ashore, and the beacon took Ted in his outboard to a dock two miles up shore where there was a telephone.

We didn't get any fishing. But I feel now I have at least STARTED to be a navigator.

I can tell a man in khaki pants and a white shirt when I see one.

No Smo . . .

IN THE department store, as I stepped on the Up escalator, I glanced aloft in time to see my fishing partner, W. C. Milne, just stepping on to the Down escalator.

It is unusual to see Milne downtown. Being of Scottish descent, he is not much interested in shopping.

He was smoking a cigarette.

The escalators were crowded. Milne was gazing off to the side, viewing the scene.

When I got within about eight feet of him, our escalators passing, I barked out sharply:

"Put out that cigarette! Don't you know there is no smo . . . !"

At which instant I perceived that it was not W. C. Milne at all, but a strange gentleman bearing only a superficial resemblance to my life-long buddy and fishing companion.

One of the great discomforts of coming up to seventy years of age is that not only do your ears begin to fail you, and your joints become entirely unreliable, so that when you jump, you land somewhere else than where you aimed, and your mind, on which you have relied all these years, starts to betray you, but you also begin to see things that aren't there at all, and miss seeing things that really are.

When I barked out my command, intended purely as a convivial joke with Milne, the stranger turned a startled stare on me, snatched the cigarette from his lips and lowered his gaze guiltily.

My fellow passengers on the escalator, both up and down, also favoured me with some funny looks. A couple of elderly ladies turned and gave me warm smiles of approval.

But I must confess the majority of those who responded to my fairly loud word of command viewed me with distaste, as much as to say, "What's the matter with you, you old blister?"

Thank goodness, a department store is a place in which you can lose yourself in the crowd almost immediately. And I was happy to reach the top of the escalator and, after a few fast turns this way and that way around a couple of circles, felt I had shaken off any identity with my error.

It would have been a good joke if it HAD been Milne, because he is always at me to quit smoking in unseemly places such as on buses, in church lobbies and other *verboten* places. And the store being liberally placarded with No Smoking signs, please, I thought I had Milne where I wanted him.

However, I soon forgot the incident, and the flushes which I had been subject to for the first minute or two subsided as I proceeded up the next escalator to the fourth floor, where I took out my shopping list and purchased two thirty-inch window blinds for the kitchen. My wife entrusts me with purchases of that kind.

I then took the escalators down to the main floor to the Notions Department, where I was to buy half a dozen dark brown hairnets for my wife. I prefer the escalators to the elevators because no matter how polite you are, allowing everybody to get on ahead of you, you end up by having some great tall man get in after you, at the last minute; and it is humiliating to short men to have their faces shoved up against a tall man's hip pockets.

As usual, when I arrived at the hairnet section of the Notions, none of the girls would pay any attention to me. It seems that at the Notions counter, men are not expected to be shopping. They are looked upon merely as strays. And when nobody paid me any mind, I let out a loud harrrumph and said: "Is anybody waiting on this counter?"

And do you know what?

The man I had mistaken for W. C. Milne was standing straight across from me, on the far side of the section, looking at me with an expression I find it embarrassing to describe.

What is worse, the girl who was waiting on HIM promptly left him and came hurrying around to me.

"No, no!" I protested generously. "Pardon me! Go ahead with the gentleman . . ."

But the gentleman, with an outraged air, turned on his heel and strode off into the crowd.

So I bought my half-dozen hairnets, dark brown, and on studying my list found that I had to go back up to the sixth floor, to the housewares, to buy a pair of those tin tongs for picking boiled potatoes out of the water, thirty-nine cents.

So back up the escalators I went again, this time with my head bowed so that by no stretch of the imagination would I see some other old friend coming down the escalator, smoking.

Now, you know how you sometimes, while reading, see a word you never saw before, a strange, queer word. And, by golly, within the next two or three days, you meet this same word five or six times, in newspapers, cookbooks, paperback mystery stories?

Sometimes it is the same with people. You notice somebody, maybe a man with a wen on the end of his nose, or a girl with a particularly Bardot style of locomotion. . .

I located the circle with the potato tongs. They were marked fifty-nine cents.

"Look, miss!" I called to one of the smocked young ladies. "Haven't you got one of these at thirty-nine . . . ?"

"I'll be with you in a moment sir," said the girl.

And who did she walk over to? At the floor-wax circle?

Yes, sir, there he was, looking less like W. C. Milne all the time.

And he was glaring at me.

I pretended not to see him.

The girl returned.

"Did you notice that man?" she asked.

"Which?" I inquired.

"The one I was waiting on?"

"Er . . . no," I said, guardedly.

"Funny. He asked me if you were a store detective."

"What a strange thing to ask," I agreed.

The tongs were fifty-nine cents, not thirty-nine.

My wife does not write very clearly on her shopping lists.

Scalawags

WE LOST our best beagle, Jeremy Diddler. The old fool. He got on a fox.

Five of us took the eight beagles out into the Caledon Hills to give the pups their first few runs on cottontail. And we included old Jeremy Diddler to show the youngsters what it was all about.

And just before dark, blamed if they didn't pick up a fox and go away. I wouldn't have thought it of Jeremy Diddler. He knows better than that.

When we realized it was a fox they were on, streaming away off to the west, we jumped in the cars and gave chase; and over toward Erin, in among the big cedar swamps, we headed them and were able to pick up seven.

But old Jeremy crossed the road ahead of us; and all alone he sang his way westward until we couldn't hear him. And it was dark.

So we sent the rest of the boys and the seven pups back to town, and Herriot and I decided to sit it out and wait for Jeremy to come back.

We drove over to the hilltop, four or five concessions back, where the fox had started. Up a dirt road, we found a kind of lane leading into a woodlot, and we backed the car into it, off the road. It was a good place to listen. We figured the fox would circle back. And once we could hear Jeremy, we would drive toward him and try to pick him up where he might cross.

In a way, this is part of the fun of beagling—sitting in the dark waiting for a scalawag to return.

I switched off the lights. Herriot made himself comfortable in the back seat for a little snooze, and I sat with the car door open, to listen.

It was a quiet night. Far off, we could hear the faint sounds of cars on the highway a couple of miles away. Now and then, some sound from one of the few farms scattered in the hills would break the stillness. But there was no far murmur that would indicate old Jeremy Diddler singing home.

Then I heard footsteps on the gravel road; and thirty feet away a match flared, and I saw two men lighting cigarettes from it. They did not see us in the car backed in off the road. They walked on.

Half an hour, three-quarters passed.

"Quarter to ten," said Herriot.

"I figure he won't be back," I said. "I bet somebody has picked him up."

"We'll sit until 10.15," suggested Herriot.

We had hardly retired back into silence before I was astonished to hear the sounds of somebody approaching behind us up the lane from the woodlot.

I nudged Herriot.

The sounds came alongside.

"Who's that?" came a gruff, startled voice.

I switched on the headlights in order to explain our presence.

As I did so, two men were revealed.

And the instant the lights went on, they broke into a run and tore out the lane to the gravel road and vanished.

"They dropped something," said Herriot, opening his door.

I got out too, and we went over to the object lying on the ground.

It was a potato sack heavy with contents.

We carried it over into the car lights and dumped it out. Five pheasants!

"Holy smoke!" said Herriot. "Poachers!"

The pheasant season doesn't open for weeks.

"They've been in the bush here," I figured, "snaring them where they roost."

"The sons of guns!" said Herriots, picking the birds up. They were dandies.

"What do we do with them?" asked Herriot.

"I can't afford to be caught with them," I asserted.

"Can we just leave them here?" asked Herriot. "Those poachers might come back looking for them."

"Not them," I assured him. "They'd just lie here and rot, or the racoons would get them.

"This woodlot," said Herriot, "is the back end of a good-looking farm out on the next road. Let's take them around to the farmer and explain."

"Right," I agreed. "And we can leave word with the farmer about Jeremy Diddler and ask him to keep an eye and ear open for him."

I took off my pullover and left it among the bushes beside the car. If old Jeremy returned, he would lie on my sweater until I came for him.

Then we drove around the concession to the farm Herriot referred to. There were lights on, and the farmer welcomed us very pleasantly.

We explained to him how we were parked, waiting for a lost beagle to come in, when two poachers came out of the bush road and dropped this bag of five pheasants.

"Do you know the game warden in this district?" I asked.

"Very well indeed," said the farmer. "You leave the birds with me, and I'll give him a ring tomorrow to come and pick them up. I'll explain the whole business to him, and it'll be all right."

"I left my sweater in the entrance of that bush road," I told him.

"I'll look there first thing in the morning," said the farmer. "And if I get him, I'll telephone you in the city."

"Collect," I said.

"That's right," said the farmer.

We stopped a couple of times before hitting the highway and listened. But no song from Jeremy.

Next morning, around 8:30, the farmer telephoned to say he had Jeremy O.K. and tied up in the barn.

"I'll be out," I said, "as soon as I can get away from the office. Or early in the evening at latest. Many thanks."

Herriot came with me for the drive. It's an hour and a half out to the hills. When he reached the farm, the farmer invited us in. There was quite a family party. A brother from New Brunswick was visiting, and there were two other women besides the farmer's wife, and three teenage boys.

"You must stay to supper," insisted the farmer's wife, after we had been out to the barn and scolded Jeremy.

It certainly smelled good.

"Why not?" said Herriot.

I knew it was the pheasants before they even appeared on the table. Roast pheasant is to roast chicken what home-made cherry jelly is to the store kind.

"I phoned the game warden all day," said the farmer. "I left a call for him. No luck. So rather than let these birds spoil, lying there in the potato sack, why, I decided we had better eat them. The game warden, under the circumstances, would likely have told me to eat them anyway."

So we had a great feast, the whole party of us, though I did feel a little conscience-stricken during my second helping.

It was nearly ten when we finally broke up; and we went and got Jeremy from the barn.

As we were about to drive off, the farmer put his hand in the window to shake hands good-bye.

"You know," he said, confidentially, "you nearly scared the stuffing out of us last night when you switched on those headlights!"

The Bang

IT HAS BEEN my lot to hear some terrific loud bangs in my life. I've been in a house hit by lightning, been blown up by five-nine shell, buried by minniewafers, and been present on auspicious occasions when engineers blew the tops off mountains and that sort of thing. Hence I can sympathize fully with the poor chap who is the hero of this little story.

It is necessary to apologize, however, before telling it, because it is slightly embarrassing. Except on the T.V., one does not discuss indoor plumbing. The whole gist of this story, however, is English indoor plumbing, with which some hundreds of thousands of Canadians were familiar during the war.

Mark you, some of the best indoor plumbing in the world is to be found in Britain, in the more modern homes and hotels. But Britain's climate is so equable and mild that buildings last far longer than they do in Canada. Thus you find hotels, like the one I have always stayed at whenever I have been in London in the two wars and in between—a grand old edifice built in the glorious reign of good Queen Victoria. Not only have its splendid stone walls survived the passing decades superbly, but so has its plumbing.

Now, few of the rooms have bathrooms attached. An Englishman is always glad of a stroll, in his dressing gown, down the spacious corridors to the room marked "Gentlemen." This large room has not merely one bath. It has four baths, each in its own ample cubicle. It does not have one toilet, but half a dozen, each in its cubicle.

Ah, well, I guess I can't stall around any longer. I'll

have to come to the point. These toilets are terrific. They have huge square solid mahogany seats, throne-like. But the majesty of them hangs overhead. There, each suspended on mighty iron brackets, are the water tanks, half the size of an upright piano. The tank is massive. It sweats. And from it dangles a sturdy chain, with a white porcelain handle to it.

These tanks are not only imposing. They are terrifying, once you have experienced them. You pull the chain. Nothing happens! You stand there in horror. Nothing happens!

Then you let go the chain. And, by gosh, Niagara or Hell's Gate is nothing to what happens. It roars, gushes, thunders. Then it clanks, clangs, burps, boils, groans, mutters. But it is that first awful gush that unnerves.

It never occurred to me that native Englishmen were as much terrified of these things as were we strangers.

But the gentleman in the room across from me decided to take a stroll, in his dressing gown, down to the Gentlemen's. It was around ten o'clock at night. The old hotel was filled with its customary eerie quiet.

He did not know, none of us knew, that already one of those mighty V-bombs that were then plastering the beloved old city had just been launched from Belgium.

At leisure, he attended to his needs. In due course, he reached and took hold on the white porcelain handle of the chain. He pulled the chain.

And at that exact instant, the V-bomb struck.

It did not strike the hotel, but out in the park in front, smashing great chunks off the hotel's masonry, injuring many people, stunning us all, rendering most of us unconscious or nearly so. I joined one of the fire-watching and rescue crews swarming through the old hotel.

On his hands and knees, crawling out of the Gentlemen's, came the guest from across the hall. We lifted him.

"I am dreadfully sorry!" he gasped, his eyes rolling in horror. "I had no idea! I pulled. And it exploded!"

We got him down to the lobby, where the more seriously shocked were being assembled. He continued to cry out about how dreadfully sorry he was. It was all his doing. He was prepared to take the whole blame.

As his wits began to return, he started to laugh.

And then we got the full account of an Englishman's inherent terror of English indoor plumbing.

"You must forgive me," he groaned amidst his laughter. "But I've been rather expecting one of the damn things to blow up for years."

Hoodoo

PETE SADGE and I were the best of friends until the spring of 1955 when he took a violent scunner against me. And if anybody ever was the innocent party, it was I.

You remember, 1955 was the year the automobile manufacturers reached a sort of climax or crescendo of fanciness in car design. You couldn't buy an ordinary plain car. Everything had to be two-tone, in gosh-awful contrasts of lemon and puce, cream and bile, pink and cadaver. Car designs consisted of sweeping lines and curves, with these colours swooping and looping. Fins were just about to be born.

Well, I was walking perfectly innocently down Yonge Street, enjoying the March sunshine of 1955 and keeping my eye skinned for any fishing-tackle stores or other interesting exhibits, when I heard my name called.

"Hiya, Greg!"

I turned toward the hail, and there was Pete Sadge driving a beautiful new model, sky-blue and heliotrope, with a jaundice-yellow roof, all aglitter, fresh from the car dealer's.

"Hi!" I responded heartily, my face no doubt expressing how impressed I was.

And Pete, turning his head to watch my reactions and enjoy my envious stare, failed to observe that traffic in front of him had come to a halt.

And he went ker-wham, scrunch, tinkle and crash into the car ahead of him.

Now, could I, by any stretch of the imagination, be considered to be at fault in this situation?

Naturally, like all the other pedestrians, I swarmed out into the stalled traffic, and pushed my way in to Pete. He had bailed out of his beautiful car and was engaged in a furious argument with the driver of the car he had bumped. There was glass all over the pavement, Pete's headlights, grill and fenders were crushed, his bumper was locked and bent over the rear bumper of the other car.

I took Pete's sleeve.

"By George, Pete," I said, "I'm terribly sorry to see . . ."

He recoiled and stared down at me with an expression of sheer malevolence.

"Oh, you!" he gritted through his teeth. "Run along, will you? Beat it!"

"But," I protested, "let me . . ."

He jerked his sleeve from my grasp.

"Go on! Get lost!" he hissed, and squared off for further violent argument with the other driver and sundry onlookers who were shouldering in to offer their testimony.

I hung around the fringe for a few minutes, as helpers tried to unstick the two cars, the police arrived, and traffic began to waggle around the blockade.

Finally, I caught Pete's eye and put on the friendliest and most commiserating expression I could. But he just turned purple and gave me a glare like a Great Dane.

So I wandered off down Yonge.

During 1956, I saw Pete three times on the street; but each time he saw me first and turned to look in a shop window until I passed.

In 1957, I was in New York on business, and when I lined up at the hotel desk to register, I noticed with anticipation that Pete Sadge was third ahead of me in line, and was having an argument with the room clerk.

It seems they had no record of any reservation for him. The clerk asked him to stand to one side while the others registered, and he would see . . .

Flushed and angry, Pete was leaning his elbow on the desk when he saw me.

"Hi!" I said, friendly.

He marched over to the row of travelling bags where the bellhops stood, picked his out of the pile, and stamped out of the lobby, down the steps and out of the hotel.

In 1958, I attended a cocktail party to meet Bennett Cerf. Being rather short in stature, I am not as aware, as are most people, of who else is at cocktail parties. I had no idea Pete Sadge was there, because he is not the bookish type.

But during the height of the crush, I heard a squeal from over in one corner, sounds of breaking glass and a loud hum of heightened conversation. So, in normal newspaper fashion, I proceeded toward the excitement to see what was going on.

When I edged and elbowed my way through the mob and got to the scene, there was Pete Sadge, looking extremely confused, and using his handkerchief to mop liquid off a woman's shoulders and back. Others were lending a hand.

"What happened?" I asked one of the helpers.

"That gentleman," said he, "turned suddenly and dumped a whole rye-and-ginger-ale down the lady's back."

I was thus right beside Pete when he happened to glance down and see me.

"Oh, Lord!" he moaned.

And like a line plunger, he just whirled and crushed through the guests toward the door.

In 1959, I saw Pete at the race track for the running of the Queen's Plate. He saw me. He turned and fled up the lawn, and I saw him go through the gate, throwing away his programme as he went. The Queen's Plate hadn't even been run. I think he went home.

Last Tuesday, this being 1961, there was all that glare

ice on the pavement after the sleet storm on top of the snow.

Everybody was walking with the greatest caution in the nine o'clock rush. Cars were crawling.

When I saw this fellow lose his footing and start to flail his arms before he went down, I had no idea, I swear, that it was Pete. When the ground is slippery and I have to move fast, I just bend my knees, slightly, thus bringing my hind end closer to the ground, so that if I do slip and fall, I haven't far enough to go to hurt myself.

So when I saw the poor fellow, his feet spinning, his arms flailing, lose his balance and go down with a real thump on to the greasy dirty, icy pavement, I went into action, scrunched down, and was therefore the first to come to his aid. I still didn't know it was Pete when I got my arms under his armpits and started to support him to his feet. His hat had fallen over his nose, besides, and his scarf had got rucked up under his nose.

A couple of others had by this time got hold of him, too, and we were hoisting him.

He shoved his hat back, and I could then see the wild eyes of Peter Sadge glaring wild at me over the top of his yellow muffler.

He reached out and shoved me away.

"You!" he cried in a broken voice.

The others stepped back, looking perplexed at me.

"You," repeated Pete, pulling the muffler down off his face, "leave me alone, will you!"

Slipping and slithering, he flung past us and away into the crowd.

"What the hell?" said one of the helpers.

"He thinks I am his hoodoo," I explained.

"His what?" asked the others.

"Hoodoo," said I.

The Gypsy

LATE IN JULY of 1951, photographer Louis Jaques
and I were sent by WEEKEND to Britain to get aboard the
bandwagon and accompany the then Princess Elizabeth
and the Duke of Edinburgh back for their tour of Canada.
It was to be a nice, comfortable assignment.

When we arrived, all members of the Royal Family were
at Balmoral, their private family castle in Scotland; and
Louis and I were tipped off that it would be good form if
we did not make ourselves too conspicuous as newspapermen, if we went up there.

Imagine our dismay, on arriving in Scotland, to find
Balmoral and the neighbouring villages crawling with
English and Scottish newspapermen and cameramen. It was
Princess Margaret's coming-of-age. And such a nuisance
were these colleagues making of themselves, creeping and
crawling amid the royal hedges, and shooting from high
spots with telephoto lenses, that the Home Secretary was
obliged to communicate with the British newspapers to ask
them to lay off.

Louis and I, instead of going to a hotel in Ballater or
any other of the villages near Balmoral, got rooms in a
private hotel on a lovely Highland hillside outside Ballater.
A fine thing it would be if the Princess and the observant
Duke were to spot us among the nuisance newspapermen,
and identify us as Canadians! So we lay low, walked the
Highland hills, saw the King pass in his station wagon, with
his dogs and guns; got glimpses of the Princess and the
Duke now and then. Our pleasant assignment, however,
was already taking a strange turn.

On Aug. 23, the proprietress met us in the doorway of our hillside hotel, as we came in from a tramp.

"There's a gypsy at the back door wants to speak to the strangers from afar."

"Pawffff!" laughed Louis.

I went out to the back door. She was not a dark, Asiatic gypsy, but to my eye just a dowdy old Scottish woman, brindle-haired, blue-eyed. She was crouched like a dog on the stone step, where she had waited all day.

"Oh, sir, you are the old one! It was you I had to speak to. Cross my palm with siller, I'll cross yours with dark news!"

"Dark news, eh?"

"Oh, sir, I have news for you. It is in your hand. Cross my palm with siller . . ."

Gypsies are lovely; old, dirty, young, dark, fair, brindled. She had an extraordinary expression in her bright old eyes. I took a florin out, and made the sign of the cross with it on her palm. Her fingers closed on the coin. I opened my hand to her.

"Oh, sir! Here is strange things. You are here on a great work. It will prosper. And the 25th of next month is the most important day. . ."

"September 25?" I laughed. "It's my birthday."

"Oh, sir, it is not that," went the gypsy in her queer sing-song. "Two days before that, all will be dark and troubled for you, and for all you have in hand. But on the 25th, that is the great day. And what you have in hand will be successful, never fear."

She closed my hand up, tweaked my coat, and scurried away like a dog, with her fat florin.

"Pawfff!" shouted Louis, when I told him. It was Aug. 23.

On Sunday, we went casually to church at Crathie, and saw the King there.

He looked like death.

Sept. 2, two specialists flew from London to Balmoral.
Sept. 9, the King went to London for one day. Sept. 15,
he returned to London. Sept. 23, he was operated on.
Sept. 25, the British and Canadian governments thankfully
announced that the Canadian visit of the Princess and the
Duke would still go on, though postponed a fortnight.

But in those mad three weeks, up to Sept. 25, I thought
of the gypsy every hectic hour.

The Hairdo

YOU'VE NOTICED my hair, of course.

Different, isn't it? Glossier. More vigorous, as they say in the commercials. Not limp and stringy, the way old men's hair usually is.

It all happened in the past week.

Up at the cottage, we have as comfortable a little summer community as you could want. There are now about sixty of us on the lake. Some of the cabins, like ours, are pretty old and warpy. But we are proud of the dilapidated look. It shows we are the pioneer families.

We are, you might say, the aristocracy of the settlement, even if we haven't got the largest boats or the most powerful engines. Even if we do still stick to oil lamps instead of having those power plants run by gasoline engines, even if we still use wood stoves instead of those gas stoves run by tanks of propane, we realize that the community respects us as the Old Originals.

We're the ones who are chosen to run the annual regatta on Civic Holiday. When the provincial government decides to raise our taxes (imagine, taxes away off there in the bush!) we're the ones who are elected to serve on the delegation.

Well, anyway, last fall when we heard that THE Joneses, and when I say THE Joneses you will know who I mean, had bought Billy Island, and were going to erect a beautiful modern cottage on it, there was considerable excitement. It was, in a sense, a shot in the arm for the lake. When we learned, further, that the new summer home, as we started to call it, was to be built by builders from the city, with an architect and all, instead of being built, as all ours were, by the McGonigles, who are the permanent settlers on the lake (there are seven families of them, all good builders, dock menders, engine repairers, guides, poachers, first-aid experts, square dancers, berry pickers and good companions), we could not deny, even in the most conservative element of us Old Originals, that a new lease of life had begun for the lake.

Furthermore, apart from the mere wealth of THE Joneses, they had three daughters and two sons. All beautiful, handsome, attractive young people, so it was said. And not a mother among the sixty of us but allowed herself the thought that there is nothing like a summer colony for the furtherance of romance. After all, who wouldn't welcome a liaison with THE Joneses?

We hardly knew Billy Island when we arrived, earlier in the season, to have hasty weekend picnics at our cottages. There in its splendour was the new Jones establishment—a great big wharf, a great big boat house and a handsome low-hung cottage painted antique brown, looking more ancient than the oldest of ours. Why, it looked like an Old Original.

Thus, when the season opened last week, the question was:

Should we invite, in the old tradition, the Joneses, as newcomers, to our cottages? Or should we await, in the new tradition, an invitation from the Joneses?

It was solved by a mass invitation which we all received in our mail boxes at McGonigle's General Store.

We were invited to a house warming.

Saturday, at 4 P.M. Tea.

Most of us waited until about 4:15 before converging on the Joneses' wharf. Then we all came in a bunch. Mr. and Mrs. Jones, dressed in the height of fashion in shorts, were on the wharf to greet us all as we arrived, and they shooed us up to the house. The Jones sons, who turned out to be elderly teenagers with the sulks, had gone to the far end of Billy Island to hide. The daughters were rather lumpy young ladies who, blushing darkly, moved among us heavily with plates of sandwiches and teetery trays of tea and coffee cups.

The first thing I noticed was that no McGonigle had built the new Jones wharf. Its stone cribs were built of two-by-fours, instead of with solid logs. The first ice of next winter would yank it from its moorings; and I predicted at once that there would be work for the McGonigles for years to come on that wharf alone.

And when I got up to the house, the Joneses being busy down on the wharf welcoming their guests, I took the opportunity to make a quick appraisal of the new mansion. Believe me, never employ an architect to design a cottage, and never bring builders from the city. Summer cottages are strictly McGonigle jobs.

Why, there was hardly a thing right in the whole . . .

I was in the kitchen when I heard the pretty hubbub of the Joneses' arrival on their front veranda. So I nipped out the back door and around, as if I had been inspecting the view from the rocks back of the rancho.

We formed ourselves into knots and clusters on the veranda and in the spacious living-cum-dining room, and Mr. and Mrs. Jones circulated around, from group to group, improving on acquaintance so briefly encountered down on the wharf. The young daughters appeared bearing trays and platters and plates of provender.

"Ah," cried Mrs. Jones, running toward me (I learned later that she had asked somebody WHICH I was), "ah, Mr. Clark! I have a special teapot for you! I understand you are a connoisseur of tea!"

"Well, ma'am," I admitted, "I can tell Darjeeling from patent tea, and Kee Mun from Young Hyson."

"Specially!" cried Mrs. Jones, whose shorts fitted her far better than any of her daughters' did. "I've prepared a SPECIAL pot for you!"

And the lumpiest daughter shyly approached and presented me with a tray all to myself. On it was a medium-sized teapot, one of those three-cup size pots. And a cup and saucer and milk and sugar.

"I NEVER take milk and sugar," I explained. "May I ask what tea this is?"

"We brought it," said Mrs. Jones, "from Ceylon. A planter we met there gave us a small packet of . . ."

And then she whisked away to some other group. It was nice to be singled out. We Old Originals.

But as soon as I poured the first cup, I detected a most curious aroma from the tea. It was certainly not Ceylon. Certainly not.

When you are singled out, you imagine people are looking at you, even if they are not. So I raised the cup and sniffed.

Lapsang Souchong, maybe? To me, Lapsang Souchong, even though gourmets rave over it, tastes like tarred rope. A friend of mine, Mrs. Macintyre, says it tastes the way the water that you pour off the finnan haddie before you put on the milk, smells.

However, we tea connoisseurs have to do more than sniff. I tasted. It was shocking.

What does one do, a tea connoisseur, in a social gathering, with a cup of tea raised in hand, when the tea tastes like . . . ?

I took a gulp. After all, the first time you eat an oyster it is a matter of courage.

I took another gulp. I felt my eyeballs start slowly to protrude. I felt my hair start to prickle.

At the veranda door appeared a Jones daughter I had not seen before. She was in a bathing suit, just come in from water skiing.

"Mom!" she yelled, being of the new generation that does not notice there is company. "Mom! Where's that little blue teapot I had the Mange Cure in?"

Then she saw it on my tray. She lolloped over and took it.

"Mange Cure?" I asked, in a curiously hollow voice.

"I use it as a shampoo," she said. "Wonderful for the hair."

When they laid me out on the veranda, I was told that the other daughters had rinsed out the pot.

But just a little may have stuck to the teapot lid.

I have had a prickly feeling in my scalp all the rest of this week.

Don't you notice my hair looks glossy, vigorous?

No?

It's probably only my imagination.

The Pike

THE MAYOR of Merville was paraded before me, the Adjutant, to make his extraordinary request.

"You mean," I demanded, "that you want this regiment to mount sentries on a pike?"

"It is a venerable pike," began the Mayor. "It is at least fifty kilos in weight. A hundred pounds! No one can remember when it was not in the pond."

"But, mon Doo," I exclaimed, dispensing for the moment with the services of Sgt. Robidoux, our battalion interpreter, "mon Doo, Monsieur le Maire, who ever heard of mounting sentries on a pike in a pond?"

"All your predecessors, if you will pardon the expression," said the Mayor, apologetically, "all the regiments who have been billeted here before you, English, French, as well as Portuguese, not only infantry, artillery and army service, but also cavalry and chasseurs have, since the start of the war, posted sentries on this pond."

"But why?" I protested.

The Mayor raised his shoulders, spread out his palms, glanced regretfully around the faces of the half-dozen soldiers with us in the barn, which was my orderly room.

"Because," he said, "of the soldiers. Grenades. Bombs. Explosives."

"Ah," I said. "Aha!"

"All over France," said the Mayor, "venerable pike of a hundred years' age, as well as carp of great size, tench, roach and dace, have been murdered by soldiers who carelessly tossed grenades into our ponds. We do not wish our great pike, which is of a hundred pounds weight, to be so destroyed."

"Where is the pond?"

"At the far end of the village," said the Mayor. "On the premises of the Lord of Merville, who is, of course, in Paris for the duration of the war."

Our D Company was billeted down at that far end.

"O.K.," I said. "I will post two sentries on the pond. Make a note of that, Orderly Sergeant?"

"Sir," said the Orderly Sergeant.

"One other matter," said the Mayor, on finding me so agreeable a gentleman. "We have in Merville here a great gander. It weighs twenty-five kilos. Fifty pounds. It is known for miles around. Merville is famous for it, also. It wanders our streets. Could you mention to your soldiers, on parade, that it is a particular gander, and not be . . . ah . . . ?"

"It shall be so noted," I said. "Orderly Sergeant?"

"Sir," said the Orderly Sergeant, making a notation in his field message book.

The Mayor was paraded from my presence out the barn door by L/Cpl. Dunc MacNeill, of Cape Breton, who was functioning as duty corporal. On L/Cpl. MacNeill's face was a lively light; and as he snapped to attention and faced me on seeing the mayor out, he assaulted me with a most insubordinate wink.

That was about 4 p.m. of the day of our arrival in Merville for a much-needed rest. By dark, the battalion was at rest; and all was quiet in Merville.

At 6 a.m. reveille, next morning, I was met on my way from my billet to the orderly room by the Orderly Officer of the day. He was hurrying.

"There's a hell of a row down at the pond," he said. "The Mayor and all the citizens are down there, and all of D Company. That gander is out in the middle of the pond acting in the strangest manner. Listen . . ."

In the stilly morning, I could hear the trumpeting of a very large bird. We hastened thither, buttoning our coats to hide our pyjamas.

Out in the middle of the pond was a large gander behaving in a most ungoosely way. Every minute or two, it would skid violently backward several feet, whereupon it would stretch its neck, flap furiously and utter strident sounds.

It was L/Cpl. Dunc MacNeill (of D Company, incidentally) the duty corporal, who suggested the means of rescue. We rigged a raft of barn doors and fencing. MacNeill himself manned it.

To the gander's leg was tied a six-foot length of fish line, a hook baited with what had been a mouse. And on the hook was the venerable pike.

Before returning it to the pond, I sent for the Captain and Quartermaster, who weighed it. It weighed only 18 pounds, or nine kilos. We also weighed the gander. It did not weigh 50 pounds, or 25 kilos. It only weighed 16 pounds.

Having thus reduced the Mayor of Merville to size, I dismissed the sentries off the pond. They had been sound asleep back in D Company's barn, anyway.

Or so the duty corporal, L/Cpl. Dunc MacNeill, told me, confidentially.

The Excuse

"IT WAS the Dewsberrys," I announced, coming from the telephone.

"Oh, dear," said my wife. "What did you say?"

"I told them," I said, "that I had been laid up the past few days . . ."

Now, the Dewsberrys are among the very nicest people we know.

A few years back, we used to see them every week. They would come to our place, or we would go to theirs; sometimes twice a week.

But you know.

TV and one thing and another. I think, sometimes, the world is growing less sociable. Or maybe we're just getting a little set in our ways. At any rate, for the past couple of years, we have been thinking up excuses whenever the Dewsberrys phoned to see if we'd run to up to see them, or that they would run down for a little while.

The darned part of it is, we don't want the Dewsberrys to feel we think any less of them. We like them as much as ever, only . . .

"We're awful!" said my wife. "Fibs, fibs, fibs."

"Well, I just said I was laid up," I explained. "That really isn't a fib. I HAVE been laid up, the way you say a ship is laid up. It doesn't mean there is anything wrong with the ship. It just means it's idle."

"I see," said my wife.

"Sort of tied up to the wharf," I elaborated.

So we sat together on the chesterfield and watched Climax, and then the news, and then half an hour or so of Jack Paar. Yawning and stretching, we let the dog out in the yard for a run, and put the kettle on. While my wife picked up the newspapers and straightened the cushions and shoved the chairs back and wandered out in the garden to pick, in the dark, a few petunias to make a bouquet for the table for breakfast, I made up a couple of Spanish-onion sandwiches, cut thin, on lean slices of the home-made bread my wife had made, with smidgins of paprika and tarragon vinegar and a dribble of Worcester sauce. And soon after midnight, we toddled happily off to bed.

I mean, that's better than having a lot of people around.

The next morning, on the bus, McKinney, a neighbour, came and sat beside me.

"I hear you've been laid up," he said, solicitously.

"Eh?" I said.

"I hope it isn't that old ticker acting up," said he.

"No, no, no," I said. "No."

All the way down he eyed me sideways. And when we parted downtown, he said:

"Now, take care of yourself, Greg."

"Sure-sure," I agreed.

Just as I turned into the office, Bain, another guy I know, hailed me and ran over.

"Say, I hear you've been laid up."

"Me?" I asked.

During the day, three more people said they had heard I had been laid up.

On the TV, just before 7 P.M., there is a sort of news roundup, and a sports editor, a local fellow, was outlining the weather prospects for the weekend, suggesting what the fishing would be like.

"Speaking of fishing," he said, "I hear that well-known fisherman, Greg Clark, has been laid up. Sorry to hear it. This is no time for a fisherman to be laid up, heh, heh, heh!"

He then went on to some other gossip.

"Good heavens!" I said.

"Well, you see?" said my wife.

At 8:20 P.M., the doorbell rang.

"Who the heck is this?" I asked, rising.

It was a florist delivery, with a box of flowers.

We opened them. The card was from Joe and Mary Higgins.

"With best wishes for a rapid recovery."

"Aw, for Pete's sake!" I cried. "I haven't been ill a day in five years!"

"See?" said my wife.

Between 8:20 and 9:45, there were six telephone calls, including one from my son sixty miles away, inquiring after my health.

At 9:45 P.M., the doorbell rang again. It was the Dewsberrys.

She had a bowl covered with wax paper. It was a bowl of the potted meat she makes so tastily, over which, in bygone years, I have been known to exclaim.

"Ah, you're up!" cried the Dewsberrys. "We've heard it all over town that you've been laid up."

"Aw, it was really nothing!" I protested, falling back on the chesterfield. My wife turned off the TV.

They didn't stay long, insisting that I must get back to bed.

"You really DO look as if you'd been through something," they told me.

So after they went, we had a couple of slices of the potted meat, with thin bread and butter and a couple of olives.

Next morning, the bus driver got up from his wheel to help me board the bus.

"Take it easy, Mr. Clark."

In the bus, Miss White, who works in the bank head office, insisted that I take her seat.

"You poor man," she said. "How long were you laid up?"

Between the bus stop and the office, two blocks, five people stopped me to tell me how thrawed out I looked. Peaked, they said.

At the office, Syd Jones, who manages everything, came straight over and told me to go on back home.

"Greg," he said, "you look all in."

"Me?" I protested.

The girls gathered around.

"We heard it on the TV last night. You go on home. You shouldn't get up so soon after a sick spell like that."

Apparently nobody had noticed I'd been around all the time.

"Please, Mr. Clark," exclaimed Miss Symington, the mothery one. "You look TERRIBLE!"

I began to feel terrible.

I went home about 10.30 A.M.

"What's the matter with YOU?" said my wife.

"How do I look?"

"Well, you look a little pale. How do you feel?"

"I feel as if I am going to be laid up."

And I was.

A Man To Remember

IN THE county in which I fish for trout and hunt the fox with beagles in winter, there lives a wicked old man who has been the terror of four townships for fifty years.

He lives on a neglected backroads farm. He has no family and only distant kin. Never a good word have I ever heard of him. In his early manhood, he was in jail for cattle theft, and he has been fined and briefly jailed many times for assault and drunkenness. He has been a bully and an outcast, a curser, a scarer of women, a character you would not wish to know under any circumstances.

Yet everybody in the county knows him, knows him well. Never a barn catches fire, never a heifer strays, but his name comes instantly to everybody's lips. Many a time I have seen him trudging along the backroads, and there is always an air of mischief about him as he glances, sideways, at my car, his mouth moving in unheard profanity. Perhaps four times in ten years I have seen him in the village. He walks hurriedly there, speaking to no one, and nobody speaking to him. If he had to pass a group of us while we were exchanging village gossip, he walked wide of us and spat tobacco as he passed.

"Lock your car," the boys say, as we pile out with the beagles on a hillside.

And I know whom they have in mind.

I overtook him on a gray, sleety day on the fourth-concession road, where the cedar swamp is blackest. He was limping badly, helping himself with a stick he had picked up.

I slowed the car beside him and asked him if he wanted a lift.

He didn't, I could see by the ugly, surly expression on his battered old face. But he had hurt his ankle badly.

He got in beside me with a profane groan.

"Aren't you So-and-So?" I asked him.

"That I am," he said emphatically.

"I've heard of you," I informed him.

"Yep, everybody for miles around has heard of me," he said. "And lots of people a long ways off from here has heard of me. If you like, I'll get out of your —— car right here!"

"Don't worry," I assured him. "I'm going right past your place."

"I don't worry," sneered the old man. "Everybody else worries. But not me."

I was silent.

"Yep," he repeated, "everybody's heard of me, and people will hear about me years from now, and long after I'm dead, too."

"Well, well," I murmured.

"I have to laugh," went on the old scoundrel. "People go to a lot of trouble to be remembered, don't they? I got neighbours who have given money and started a library and donated to everything. There's people around here who have gave windows to the churches. They get great big tombstones put up to them. But does anybody remember them in five years?"

"I see, mmm-hmmmm," I put in.

"Well, in fifteen years does anybody remember them?" he demanded, twitching sideways to give me a contemptuous glance. "But by ————! They'll remember me! They'll tell stories about me fifty years from now. There's people not born yet who will know about me. They'll know how I looked. They'll know where I lived. They'll tell about the fights I been in."

I pretended to be busy with the steering, on the rough swamp road.

"Fights," he said, "and the barns I been accused of firing, and the cattle stolen. Eh! Already, they got more stories about me than I ever really done. They're building up a bigger tombstone than anybody's got, long before I'm dead. When I was a young kid, I decided I wanted to be remembered. Well, by ——, they'll remember me!"

I could see his face in the rear mirror. It was an evil old face, full of cunning and malice. But it was lit by a glow of satisfaction as he stared out through the windshield.

We came up the hill to his lane. His dirty old house showed up shadowy through the sleet. I drew off the gravel and he pushed the door open and lowered himself cautiously to the ground.

He slammed the car door.

He did not say thanks. He did not even give me a parting glance.

What else can I do but remember him?

Finders—Keepers

"WHOA!" yelled Dandy Daniels in his quavery old voice. "Hurroo! Hey, whoa-up! Pull up!"

Dandy is my eighty-, ninety-, nobody-knows-how-old friend whom I take for drives.

"Back up!" commanded Dandy. "There's a bag full of something on the side of the road back there."

"It'll be junk, Dandy," I said.

"Not on your life!" he insisted. "I caught a good look at it. Might be a bag of potatoes fell off some truck."

So I backed carefully, one wheel on the shoulder, as the traffic swished past us. We were on our way home from a farm auction Dandy had heard about. He loves farm auctions. Been going to them for sixty, seventy years. He never buys anything. He knows no more about farming than any other city slicker. But it affords him some weird and wonderful thrill to sit on a kitchen chair out on the lawn, in the front row of the assemblage, and see the stock, implements and household effects disposed of in the lovely long-drawn-out drama of a farm auction on a fine sunny summer day. I think he enjoys the caution, the canniness, the craft, the cunning displayed by his fellow men and women as the bids rise, dime by dime. Dandy is a congenital tightwad.

"Easy!" he directed, as I backed the car. He craned out the car window.

"There it is!" he cried. "Just pull alongside of it and we'll wait until there is a lull in the traffic, so nobody will see us pick it up."

"Dandy!" I protested.

"Finders — keepers," he asserted.

"There's a Provincial Police depot down the highway a few miles," I informed him. "We'll just turn it in there, if there's anything valuable in it."

"The heck we will!" cried Dandy, turning an outraged face on me. "I saw it first. I found it. I'll decide what I'll do with it!"

He directed me to the right spot and halted me. I prepared to bail out on my side.

"Psst!" warned Dandy. "Sit still until the traffic eases off."

He twisted his old bones around to peer out the back window.

"O.K., now!" he commanded, and opened his door. I got out and went around the back of the car.

It was an ordinary large jute potato bag, and it was stuffed rigid with some sort of merchandise. Its neck was tied tight with twine.

"Easy!" warned Dandy, glancing up and down the highway. "Don't touch it yet."

"Now, Dandy . . ." I objected.

"Do what I tell you!" he hissed, alertly swivelling his head.

He opened the rear door of the car.

"Now!" he rasped, seizing one end of the bag. I took the other, and we tossed it on to the floor of the car.

Dandy, flushed with excitement and exertion, slammed the door.

"Good!" he gasped. "Nobody saw it."

We got back in the car.

"There wasn't much in it," I remarked. "It was pretty light."

"Who knows?" said Dandy. "It might be bedding. Lovely

soft linen sheets, or maybe patchwork quilts like we saw going for two bucks at that auction!"

"Maybe," I offered, getting back on the highway, "it's full of excelsior. Or chicken feathers."

"Not a chance," said Dandy, flushed with the excitement of new possession. "Do you know what I bet it is? One of those eiderdown sleeping bags these here sportsmen take camping. Do you know how much they cost? A hundred and twenty dollars."

"You can get a sleeping bag for ten bucks," I submitted. "Who would put a beautiful eiderdown sleeping bag in a potato sack?"

"By golly!" exclaimed Dandy. "Do you know what I bet it is? A bag of radishes. Didn't you notice how nubbly it was when you picked it up? And radishes are just coming in season. Man, do I like a feed of good big hot red radishes!"

"What would you do with a potato bag full of radishes?"

"My grocer," explained Dandy, "would take the surplus off me. I often do little deals like this with my grocer."

"Maybe," I supposed, "it is a bag of spinach."

"Spinach!" scoffed Dandy. "Pah!"

"Look, Dandy dear," I reasoned. "There is a moral angle to this. I suggest we drop in at the Provincial Police depot. It's only a couple of miles now."

"You look!" retorted Dandy, hotly. "I'll deal with the morals. I know a lot more about morals than you do. Wait till you're my age before you start moralling me. I've lost hundreds of things in my life. And did anybody ever give them back to me?"

"You're supposed to advertise . . ." I attempted.

"Let THEM advertise!" snorted Dandy. "And I'll make darn sure I don't look in the newspapers for the next few days."

"You'll excuse me, Dandy," I persisted. "But I am compounding a felony in this matter. I helped lift the goods into the car. It is my car. And I am driving it. I have to demand a share of the responsibility."

"Aha!" piped Dandy. "A nice way of putting it. You want a share of the goods!"

As we approached the Provincial Police depot at an intersection of the highway, I slackened speed.

"I warn you," said Dandy. "If you turn in here, I'm through with you!"

Which would be a bad thing for both of us. Who would take Dandy for drives then?

I put on speed and hastened past the depot.

"All I hope is," said Dandy, "it isn't parsnips."

"No," I comforted him. "Parsnips aren't in yet, for a long time."

"I still bet," mused Dandy, "it is one of those eiderdown sleeping bags."

"Not likely."

"Or patchwork quilts, like we saw at the auction back there."

"Not very likely, in a potato sack."

"Patchwork quilts," dreamed Dandy, "in Paisley patterns. Mostly red and light blue."

He twisted around and rested one arm on the back of the seat and gazed fondly and speculatively down on the sack.

When we reached the city and drove into Dandy's side drive, we carried the sack eagerly into the back yard. Dandy himself untied the twine with trembling hands, and we peeped in.

We then up-ended the bag and dumped it on the grass.

Waste paper, pop bottles, lunch cartons, paper napkins, bits of sandwich crust.

Examining the bag closer, I found a small tag on the corner.

"Department of Highways," it read. "Cleanup crews."

"Why, Dandy!" I cried joyously. "We've helped the Provincial Highways Department collect up the trash!"

"You think you're pretty smart, don't you?" said Dandy bitterly.

And went in and slammed the screen door at me.

The Sneer

I TOOK my seat down at the back of the bus, where the seats face each other. On looking up, I was greeted by the lady sitting directly opposite me with the most deliberate sneer I have ever been subjected to.

In the instant before I averted my startled gaze, I took in that she was a well-dressed lady of something less than middle age, with a parcel or two on her lap.

But the sneer! There could be no mistaking it, and no mistake but that it was aimed straight at me. Personal. Her eyes were literally dancing; but her nose curled up and her lips writhed in an expression so contemptuous, I was staggered.

I kept my eyes on the bus floor while I hastily chased back through my mind to try to imagine what I might ever have done to earn such an affront. In public, too.

No gentleman, it is said, ever gives offence unintentionally. But in the newspaper business, we sometimes give offence thoughtlessly. For instance, I might refer to somebody as "deaf as a post." And instantly, I have offended all who are hard of hearing. For who wants to be likened to a post? Or I might lightly use the word "nitwit"; and 10,000 people, who secretly think of themselves as nitwits, subconsciously are offended, and become hostile to me. These are the things that haunt a newspaperman's life. Especially when he is sitting in a crowded bus and the lady opposite sneers at him, practically out loud.

I kept my eyes on the floor until I felt she was no longer looking at me; and then I ventured another swift glance. Her face was flushed. And averted.

But I knew she knew I was looking at her. Her eyelids lowered and rose; and even that was contemptuous, though she was not looking at me. She was flushed, I figured, with pride. She had given me a sneer, and it had given her deep satisfaction. She was now on her way home; and when she got there, she would stride triumphantly into the living room and announce to her husband, children and mother-in-law: "I sat across from Gregory Clark in the bus just now, and gave him a sneer right to his face!"

H'mmmm! I had a faint, a very faint recollection of having seen the lady before. But a newspaperman sees so many faces . . .

Who the dickens was she? And what had I done, or said, or written, to rouse such animosity?

Before I could avert my gaze, she turned, and again I was favoured with the hot, glinting eyes, and the lips parting in the same twisted, deliberate sneer.

As I lowered my eyes, I felt myself flushing in my turn. It was a flush of anger as well as of humiliation. For Pete's sake, wasn't one sneer enough? Did she have to sit there all the way home and keep sneering? As I glared at the bus floor, my mind still chased around, like a gopher looking for its hole, trying to place the woman, speculating a little frantically on what I had been guilty of. Was she the wife of somebody I owed money to? What debts did I owe? Had I said something mean about someone lately? By golly, was she some distant relative, maybe, and I had forgotten to send a wedding present to her daughter?

I raised my eyes once more for a good, straight look. This time, I would try to identify her.

Boom! She was sitting there, looking straight at me. And the instant our eyes met, she immediately gave me the full, deliberate, twisted sneer.

Flesh and blood can just stand so much. Oh, so you

want to sneer, do you? Well, how's this? And I gave her a sneer straight back, jerked to my feet, stamped up the bus toward the front, where I hung on the hand rail with my back to her until I reached the next main crossing street. There I dismounted, with never a backward glance, and waited four minutes for the next bus. Which I took, at a cost of ten cents.

After supper, I was called to the telephone. It was Geordie MacKay, an old, old friend of mine whom I haven't seen much of in recent years.

"Look here, Greg, I've got a bone to pick with you."

"Yes?"

"You were very rude to my wife this afternoon."

"Your wife?"

"On the bus. She sat across from you."

Holy Nellie! Of course. That was Geordie's wife. I had only seen her a few times in my life; and the last time, four or five years back.

"Geordie . . .," I said, at a loss to know how to start.

"She says," said Geordie, "that you glared at her."

"But . . ."

Geordie started to laugh.

"She was on her way home from the dentist's," he hooted. "Her upper jaw was frozen by the dentist, and she was trying to smile at you. But she had no feeling in her lip."

I ran out and got in the car and drove to Geordie's. And Mrs. MacKay and I sat smiling at each other until 11 P.M.

The Backfire

"THERE ARE three fireplaces in this house," I declared to all my assembled womenfolk, "and I haven't seen one of them lit in seven or eight years!"

The ladies observed me in silence, hoping I would let the matter drop at once, as I often do when they observe me in silence.

"I," I announced, "am going to lay in a couple of cords of firewood. There's nothing, at this time of year, like a fragrant, bright fire of apple wood to greet . . ."

"Where," interrupted the head mistress, "are you going to put the wood?"

"Down cellar," I replied. "There's . . ."

"What will you move," asked another, "to make room for it? Your tool bench, maybe? Or those stacks of old books?"

"Why, there's . . . uh . . ." I pointed out.

"None of the fireplaces works," declared a third member of the rules committee. "This one in the living-room back-fires."

"The one in the den," said another, "suffers from fallout. Things fall out of it. All the time."

"Ladies," I commanded, "sit down, please."

Because they were all standing up; which is a mean way women have of dominating. If you can get them sitting down, you have a chance.

Cautiously, they sat.

"Ladies," I said, "on my way into town today from my bird-watching trip, I passed through one of those farm areas out beyond the suburbs which is being got ready for a new housing development. The fences have been brushed aside. Bulldozers are floundering all over the landscape, pushing down the hillocks, shoving up the gullies, squashing the underbrush, smashing down the trees, and making all lovely and beautiful, in the human sense, for human habitation. In other words, flatter than pea soup on a plate."

The ladies all nodded their heads in acknowledgment of the delicacy of my allusion.

"Now," I continued, with emotion, "in one corner of the farm is the orchard. An old, gnarled apple orchard. The trees have been cut down, and the farmer was sawing the trunks and limbs into billets and chunks."

Silence.

"There is no wood, ladies," I cried, "that burns with a lovelier fire than apple wood. Its flames are coloured, blue, green, red. They spit and spark and mutter. They give off a delicious aroma. To come, on a chill autumn evening, to sit by a fire of apple wood is as sweet and old-fashioned as needlepoint on a chair, like an old afghan your grandmother knitted, like a book you read in your girlhood, sitting in a hammock . . ."

Well, the ladies got up and went about the house studying the various fireplaces, hoking at them, poking at them, pulling and shoving the old, corroded dampers while rust and soot tinkled down.

And I, the following morning, drove out the highway to the housing development I had passed.

And sure enough, there was the farmer with the bucksaw heartily toiling away at the tumbled apple trees, cutting the fat gnarled limbs and the stout hole-pitted trunks into billets.

"Ah," I said, coming to the last remaining fence, "it's a sad business, eh, the end of an orchard?"

"Aye," he said, "it is."

"What are you going to do with the wood?" I asked.

"Firewood, I suppose."

"Can I buy some?"

"I wouldn't wonder," said he.

"What price are you asking?" I inquired, "say, for two cords?"

The farmer scratched his head and gazed around the ruined acres. Bulldozers whuffed in the distance, trucks snorted and ground.

"You'd arrange your own pickup?" he asked.

"I'd get a truck," I said, "and take it right from here."

He did some more calculating, again gazing, a little forlornly, I thought, across his riven land.

"What would you say," he said, "to ten bucks a cord?"

I was delighted. To hide my satisfaction, I got out my wallet and handed him two tens.

"Would you pile it right here?" I pointed. "And I'll leave it to you to measure the cords. Four by four by eight, eh?"

"Correct," said he, pocketing the $20. "Have you any choice of wood? These are snows. Those over there are russets."

"How about a mixture, a cord of each?"

"Correct," said he. "What time will you be back?"

"I can get a truck by 4 P.M., I imagine," I said. "Could you have it piled by then?"

"Correct," he said.

So I drove happy back to town, and in the yellow pages got a trucker who said he would do the job for $10. I arranged to go with him, in the cab, to save time. And at 4 P.M. we drew up at the orchard.

There had been some misunderstanding, apparently. The pile was not where we had arranged.

I walked across the field to a man on a bulldozer that

had broken down and he was sitting in it waiting for a repairman.

"Where's the farmer," I asked, "who was cutting in the orchard?"

"No idea," said he. "Better go and ask at the office."

He pointed to a shack at the far end of another field.

I walked across the mud and heaps of blasted earth to the hut.

There were two young men in hunting shirts bent over large blueprints on temporary tables made out of farmhouse doors.

"The farmer?" said they, with surprise. "There's been no farmer around here for a good many years. This land's been owned by a syndicate since 1949."

"Well, if not the farmer," I suggested, "then the man who was cutting up the orchard this afternoon?"

"Oh, him," said the young men. "He's not the farmer. He's just a character that came by last week looking for a job. So we gave him the job of cutting up the orchard wood."

"Well, he sold me two cords," I announced.

"HE sold you?" said both men. "That apple wood belongs to the president of the syndicate. He wants it for his fireplaces."

"Where can I find him?"

"The president?"

"No, the other fellow."

"Oh, he came in around two o'clock and we paid him off. He said he was on his way."

So I paid off the trucker, and he drove me home.

And since the ladies haven't brought up the question of the fireplaces, neither have I.

The Hitch-hiker

THE OLD BOY on the side of the road, thumbing, was possibly a Character. Maybe even a Philosopher.

As a rule, I don't pick up hitch-hikers any more, unless they are in uniform. The last few times I have had fleas, it was due to having picked up Characters.

But this old boy, as I rapidly approached him, had an Interesting look. He might well be an Interesting Character. And when, at about 40 yards, I detected at his feet a nice, clean, fresh-looking haversack, and when I perceived he had a fine, red, tanned face, and that his wispy white hair blowing in the wind could hardly be sticky, I threw overboard my prejudices and began to slacken speed. An Interesting Character is always a welcome pick-up. And sometimes you catch the top bracket of hitch-hikers, who are Philosophers.

"Hi!" I called out the window, noting with delight that he was carrying a gnarled walking stick.

He opened the door and lifted in his haversack.

In his wind-blown old face he had bright, sharp eyes; and all the wrinkles about them were from good nature.

Slowly he reached out and closed the door, glancing behind.

"Careful," he said. "Cars coming."

"I'll be careful," I assured him cheerily. "You've picked a careful driver."

"That I noticed," he said, "when I seen you coming in the distance."

"Aha! You pick your cars, eh?"

He was still turned to watch rearward.

"Yes, sir," he agreed. "I avoid these new-model cars."

"Well, heck," I protested. "This one isn't so ancient—1950."

"It's O.K. now," said the old boy. "Nothing coming."

So I steered back off the shoulder and stepped on the gas. He continued to watch back.

"You're not nervous are you?" I inquired, to get the ball rolling. "You can't be a hitch-hiker and nervous."

"No, sir, I ain't nervous," he said, turning and making himself comfortable. "And I am a regular, you might say a practising, hitch-hiker."

I knew I had a Philosopher.

"Well, sir," I said, "how far am I to have the pleasure of your company?"

"To Porter's Corners, if you're going that far," he replied. "Twenty-six mile. You come over a rise, and there's a big swamp spread out below . . ."

"I know it well," I assured him.

"Full of rabbits," he said. "Cottontail and swamp hare, both. AND foxes."

"I don't doubt that," I said.

A car whipped past us from behind, and the driver and the woman beside him both glared at us.

Indeed, they turned to glare back, after they had passed.

"What's eating them?" I put in.

"Oh, it's hard to say," said my Philosopher. "No accounting for manners on the highway, is there?"

Another car overtook us and swished past. The driver turned and motioned with his thumb, backwards.

"What's the matter with him?" I snorted.

"Guess he wants you to speed up," suggested the Philosopher.

"I'm hitting fifty," I stated. "That's my speed. And also the law's."

"They're always in a rush," admitted the old boy, turning to glance behind. "Nobody behind you. You ain't forming no queue."

"I agree," I said, "that people who dawdle on the highway are the cause of more accidents than anybody else. A man going forty is bound to build up a tail of half a dozen or a dozen cars behind him. And trying to pass him results in more accidents than all the speed in the world. But tell me. About foxes. What is your interest in foxes and the big swamp at Porter's Corners? Are you a sportsman?"

"Well, no," said my kindly old passenger. "I guess I am what you might call a naturalist or something. I just like to set in the swamp and look and listen."

"Well, now!" I exclaimed, delighted. "Orchids? Birds?"

"Yes and no," said my Philosopher. "They're all part of it. Just setting and listening and watching."

"You a farmer?"

"No, I spent my life as a sawmill hand," said the old boy. "But I been retired now twenty years or so. Living on my daughter, a fine woman."

"You interest me," I declared. "How about this business of sitting in a swamp, looking and listening? Tell me about this."

Two cars from behind overtook us and sped past. The first was driven by a man who had three women passengers. They all glared back at me, and waved their hands in a menacing fashion. The second car was full of small children in the rear window, and they, wide-eyed, waved and yelled and pressed their noses against the glass.

"For goodness' sake," I announced, looking at my speedometer.

"This craze for speed," said my companion.

So I put on five miles and brought her up to fifty-five.

"Not too fast," cautioned my Philosopher, taking a gander out the back window as I accelerated.

But I held it at fifty-five, as we chatted about swamps and orchids and screech owls and foxes; and presently we overtook a thin-necked gentleman with large ears going about forty.

"Look at this," I pointed out to my passenger. "Dawdling along at his own sweet pace."

We swished past him.

In a moment, I became aware that the dawdling gentleman was right on my tail. He moved out to pass.

"Just look at that!" I cried. "We pass him and right away . . ."

The dawdler shot past me. And hardly had he passed me before he began to slacken speed.

"Why, the son of a gun!" I gritted. "Imagine that! Going forty or less, and now . . ."

I veered out and leaped past him. He gave a couple of toots on his horn, put on speed, passed me, and hardly had he passed before he again slackened speed so that I nearly ran him down.

"One of these here traffic evangelists," commented my Philosopher, "trying to teach others how to drive, eh?"

I veered out and passed him, and as I did so I turned to give him an indignant glare. He was motioning energetically toward the back of my car.

I drew over to the shoulder. He pulled up behind me. I got out.

"You got a dog," he called from his window, "on your back bumper."

Sure enough, there was a hound squatted cosily on my back bumper, slapping his tail.

"Well," explained my old Philosopher, as he bailed out.

"Nobody will pick me up with a hound. So I trained him to hide in the bushes, and jump on whenever I get aboard."

"Old-model cars . . ." I reflected.

"I pick 'em," said he, "for their bumpers. I know my models."

The hound's name was Bojangles. We took him in the car. A fine, wise Redbone he was. And I let the Philosopher and Bojangles out at their favourite entry to the Porter's Corners swamp.

And I wished to God I could have gone with them.

The Hat Box

I WENT to the airport to meet Lawrence Wild, and when I saw him coming down the ramp steps from the plane, he had some kind of black object held awkwardly in front of him.

When he got closer, I perceived that it was a black and gold striped cardboard hat box. It is not like Lawrence to carry parcels of any kind. He was carrying this one very badly, held out in front of him as if it contained vipers.

He had flown to meet me here. And from here we were taking the night train to New York, where we were going to spend two or three days shopping all over the place for a high-powered rifle with telescopic sights for Lawrence to use on a big-game hunting trip into northern British Columbia.

Why me? Well, Lawrence and I went to school together about 50 years ago. He still thinks I am a great authority of firearms, because in those days I owned a single-shot .22, and he has consulted me on all matters pertaining to weapons ever since.

"Hi!" I welcomed him. "What have you got there?"

"Oh, nothing," said Lawrence, handing it to me. "Hold it for a minute, will you?"

He got rid of the hat box with obvious relief, and I held it by the ornamental gold and black cord with which it was tied.

After thanking me for agreeing to come to New York with him—which was at his expense, since he owns a machine-tool factory, seven gas stations, a book shop, a riding school and about 40 pieces of real estate in his home town—he raised his hand and beckoned in thin air. And a redcap appeared as if by magic.

Now, you or I could scamper all over an airport for twenty minutes without being able to find a redcap. But wealthy men are psychic. It looks to me as if they just THINK a redcap into existence.

"Get my bags, will you?" said Lawrence, giving the redcap his checks.

"I'll go and drive my car around here to the exit," I said.

"Give me the box," said Lawrence.

"I'll just put it in the . . ."

"No, no," said Lawrence, "let me have it."

"What the Sam Hill is in it?" I demanded, as Lawrence took it gingerly, holding it away from him.

"Oh, just a hat," said he. "I bought a hat in New York last March when I was down. And when I got it home, I found it had a flaw, a sort of smudge in the front of the crown."

"What kind of hat?" I asked.

"A homburg," said Lawrence, embarrassed. "Black homburg. Goes with formal clothes. Wear it to weddings and funerals and that sort of . . ."

I went and got the car and brought it around, leaving Lawrence in the lobby standing with the hat box dangling from his half-outstretched arm.

When the redcap put Lawrence's handsome luggage in beside my junk, in got Lawrence, and he held the hat box on his lap.

"Chuck it in the back seat," I said, for it was an hour's drive to the railway station downtown.

But he just held it on his lap.

"I wrote these hat people," said Lawrence, "and they said to mail it back to them and they would replace it with another. Twenty-six dollars I paid for it."

The rifle he was going to buy would likely cost him over $500.

"Why didn't you mail it back?" I asked.

"I wrote them and said I would bring it in on my next visit to New York," said he. "Pretty fragile, a hat, to send all the way to New York, customs and all."

We got to the railway station with an hour to spare. A redcap, ready and waiting, took charge of our baggage and undertook to see it safely aboard the sleeping car for us while I put my car in a garage nearby and we could sit around until the sleeping cars were ready.

"Give him the box," I suggested.

"No," said Lawrence, "I'll just hang on to it. It's no trouble."

I left him in the main concourse while I parked the car, and he was standing self-consciously holding the gaudy black and gold box the way a first-time father holds a wet diaper.

When I rejoined him, I offered to take the blame thing for a change.

"It's no trouble," said Lawrence, shifting it to the farther hand.

"You must be awfully fond of homburgs," I said.

"No," said he, "but I just don't like spending $26 on a hat and then finding a defect in it."

In about twenty minutes, the gateman said we could go aboard the sleeper. The porter at our car tried to take the box from Lawrence as we mounted the steps.

"I'll take it," said Lawrence stiffly.

In the morning, when we lined out of our roomettes, there was Lawrence with the hat box in hand. The porter had taken all our other pieces fifteen minutes before and stacked them in the vestibule.

In the gloom of Grand Central's bowels, we got a redcap in about two minutes, which is miraculous. Lawrence carried the box up the escalator, lifting it high so as not to bump. In the taxi, he carried it on his lap. At the hotel, he wouldn't let the porter take it, along with our other gear. When we registered, he set it on the counter. When a bell-boy, on being given our key, reached for the box, Lawrence beat him to it.

"I'll look after this," he said.

We got to our room and chose beds.

"Now, look," I said. "The first thing let's do is get rid of that hat."

"That is exactly what I was going to suggest," said Lawrence.

Thus, eager to be out in the tall, raging excitement of New York, with the prospect of visiting five or six gun shops great and small, we went down the elevator and out the lobby, Lawrence bearing his hat box with a little more swagger, now that he was about to be rid of it.

It was no great distance to the swank Fifth avenue shop where Lawrence had bought it, but he insisted on taking a taxi.

We entered the trim, lordly shop.

"I'd like to see the man," said Lawrence, "from whom I got this homburg last March. Short, middle-aged, white crew cut."

The salesman was produced.

"I bought this hat last March," said Lawrence, "and when I got it home, there was a flaw right on the front of the crown. So I wrote you . . ."

The salesman took the box and placed it on a showcase, and untied it. He lifted the lid.

The box was empty.

Lawrence stared into space for a long moment.

"I'll mail it to you when I get back to Canada," he said, finally. "I just remember I forgot to put it in."

Roulette

LET'S START the New Year with a clean conscience. Ever since those confessions during the investigation of the fixed quiz shows, my conscience has been so red, swollen and inflamed, I have hardly been able to sleep.

Well, that may be stretching it a bit. It would take more than conscience to disturb my sleep. By inheritance and a natural aptitude, I am a dedicated sleeper. As a younger man, I worked out a plausible theory that the purpose of life was to allow you just sufficient waking hours in order to get pleasantly tired and appreciate the beauty of sleep.

By inheritance, too, I am a snorer. My father and mother were famous throughout a large family connection for the harmoniousness and splendid volume of their snores. My mother was of the school that starts low and gentle, and gradually, inch by inch, works up to a sort of crescendo, each snore getting louder and longer until, reaching explosion point, she blew up, muttered, rolled over and started all over again. My father, on the other hand, was a steady snorer. His was, you might say, the beat of the duet. Like a bass fiddle or a tuba, his deep, vibrant notes never changed in volume or pitch. It was like the sound of a sump pump, or of the walking beam of a side-wheeler steamboat. It beat out the tempo for the fanciful obbligato of my mother; and my fondest memories of childhood are those of the night, and these sounds so blissfully associated with slumber. For they often waked me up and gave me a fresh opportunity to enjoy the sensuous pleasure of falling asleep again.

None of these characteristics or, if you like, failings of

mine, was known to the small company of a dozen or more young war correspondents whom I joined in Sicily, in 1943, in time for the landing of the Canadians on the toe of Italy.

They were young fellows in their late twenties and early thirties. I was an elderly buster in my fifties. There was Ralph Allen, a redhead, who became editor of *Maclean's Magazine*. There was Ross Munro, ace reporter of the Canadian Press news agency, a kindly and bespectacled young man with a most admirable respect for the aged, who has become publisher of *The Winnipeg Tribune*; William Stewart, of Canadian Press, whom I presently tried to adopt as my son, only to find his parents were still living; Wallace Raeburn, now a London, Eng., columnist; J. A. M. Cook, Richard Sanburn, the late Matthew Halton, and several others.

Our first night together was in the town of Reggio, in Italy, the evening of the Canadians' successful first landing on the European mainland.

We were all crowded into one large room of a windowless, gutted house.

When our dispatches were filed with the army censors, we laid our bedrolls on the floor.

"Hey!" said a rough voice in my ear.

It was Ralph Allen, shaking my shoulder.

"Roll over!" he suggested curtly.

"O.K.," said I, relapsing thankfully.

"Here! Whoosh! Whisht!" hissed a voice in my ear.

It was Stewart.

"Roll over!"

"O.K.," I thanked him, snuggling.

And that is the last I know of my first night in Italy.

But what happened was this. After about fifteen minutes, Allen got up and hung a blanket over the window frame and lighted a candle.

The others were all sitting up dolefully in their bedrolls.

"Do we kill him," asked Cook, "or just move him out into the yard?"

Ralph Allen was searching his pants pockets.

He produced his roll of Italian occupation lire with which all correspondents were heeled.

"Listen," commanded Allen, of the figures crouched in their bedrolls on the floor. "Count how many he goes."

I went seven snores. Paused. Changed gears.

"Count," said Allen.

I went sixteen. Paused. Changed gears.

"Roulette," said Allen, standing in the candle light, his fist full of new Italian money. "When he finishes this run, I bet on nine for the next run."

Up scrambled all the others, searching their pockets for their money.

They formed a circle around me, using my gently undulating frontal expanse as the gaming table.

And there in the candle light, in the town of Reggio, was born the game of snore-roulette.

Far into the night, my young colleagues gambled, since they could not sleep; and they say I performed beautifully, the perfect roulette machine that could not be fixed. Sometimes I ran long series, sometimes short. When one would gamble that I would throw a three, I would throw five sixes in a row. And just when they figured I was all tuned up for a run of tens, I would snort out a two. Ralph Allen won 1,400 lire ($14 in real money) that night before the candles gave out, though I did not.

From there on, my social success was assured. As we progressed up through Italy, I was invariably given the best floor in the largest rooms of ruined farmhouses, villas and schools. My young friends encouraged me to go to bed early and get well warmed up by the time the game was to start. Visiting officers from the regiments were entertained.

It was my conducting officer, Capt. Gordon Hutton, M.C., of Calgary, who planted in my innocent mind the seeds of what might have been a moral disaster for both of us.

"Do you realize," he asked me, as he drove me around the mountains of Campbasso, "that thousands of lire changed hands over your belly last night?"

"Mmmm," said I, remembering only my bedroll and its snug comfort.

"Do you realize," he demanded, "that millions of lire may depend on your snores before this campaign is over?"

"Wouldn't wonder," I said, yawning, and wondering what time it was.

"I," said Captain Hutton, "lost four hundred lire on you last night."

"Sorry," said I, for I was very beholden to Hutton for safe-conducting me all over the war zone.

And then we both got the same idea at the same instant.

Hutton drove the jeep off to the side of the road while we laid our plans.

We would both memorize a series of numbers. We would practise it for several days as we drove together around the battle front.

And when we had got the series of numbers thoroughly memorized, and on a night when there was a big gathering playing on me, Hutton would wake me up by the only known device by which I can be roused, which is to bend my little finger shut and then squeeze.

"How will I know you are really awake?" demanded Hutton.

"Bend my other little finger until I yell," I explained. "And then you'll know I am awake and ready to go as soon as I feign sleep again."

The fell plot was complete. In the town of San Vito, it was put into operation. The house was full, as they say in the gambling casinos. It appeared to me there were thirty in the game when Hutton squeezed my other little finger and I woke yelling in their midst.

Then I lay back and feigned sleep. Hutton began betting on the first series, a seven. He had won six straight, and taken nearly all the lire in the house when I began sweetly dreaming of all the lire he had piled up on the floor in front of him. Eleven was the next number.

Hutton bet the works, to take the works.

I went twenty-nine, the longest in my entire record, before pandemonium waked me.

And the next day, Capt. Hutton applied to be transferred to Matthew Halton as conducting officer, instead of me.

I am happy to say that I can't be fixed, thanks not to my principles but to my weaknesses.

Magda

THE VANCOUVER SUN in 1952 shook the stuffing out of the newspaper profession across Canada by deliberately printing the same identical news story about the day's fighting in Korea three days running: and not a single reader called up the paper to point out the error.

What is news? The dictionary says it is the report of any recent event or situation. A good news editor will say that news is what the public will read. If the public doesn't read it, to whom is it news?

Ah, an editor's job is often like whistling through a knot hole. Main Johnson was the editor of a paper I worked for that had about half a million circulation. He had to buy a good deal of syndicate material from American and British agencies. And among the features he was offered was a whopping five-part serial story, full of very catchy photographs and art work, all about Magda Lupescu, the poor but beautiful dancing girl, and King Carol of Romania, her lover.

It was a dandy. Main Johnson bought it and scheduled it to run five weeks. And across the bottom of the front page of the magazine section, the issue of the week before the Magda Lupescu feature was to start, he had a great big streamer line set, in type two inches high:

WHAT ABOUT MAGDA LUPESCU?

When the paper came off the presses, one of the first copies was always taken to the office of the publisher, which was down on the third or quiet floor of the newspaper building.

The publisher was an elderly gentleman widely respected

for his acumen in all things. When he shook open the new issue, fresh off the presses, he beheld across the whole width of the front page this big bold question:

WHAT ABOUT MAGDA LUPESCU?

After one brief glance, he reached for his telephone and asked Main Johnson to please drop down to see him. Right away.

When Main entered, the publisher pointed wryly at this big bold streamer.

"Ah," said Main, "a wonderful feature. In five parts. Beautifully illustrated. New and exclusive pictures. Starting next week."

The publisher shook his head sadly.

"I," he said gently, "don't LIKE Magda Lupescu. Furthermore, I don't like King Carol. In fact, I don't like this feature."

There was a silence that only editors know.

"Throw it away," said the publisher briefly.

All of us who were around that day will never forget the confusion. The whole paper for next week's issue was already made up—type set, engravings made, everything. The Lupescu story was the feature. A new feature had to be found, instanter. All promotion and circulation-booster posters had to be called off. It was a riot. One way or another, a new feature was found and rushed into production—art, layout, typography.

But oh!—there were those half-million papers already off the press, with the challenging question:

WHAT ABOUT MAGDA LUPESCU?

We sat and waited.
The next week's issue came out.

— 159 —

We hunched up, prepared for the storm.

We waited a day, two days, three days.

We waited all week. Not a thing happened. Nobody called up, nobody wrote. Not a reader, not an agent, not a romantic, not a Carol-lover, not a soul.

Finally, two weeks exactly from the date of issue of the big bold question, came a postcard from a reader in Waskesiu Lake, Sask.:

"Okay. I'll bite! WHAT ABOUT MAGDA LUPESCU?"

The Thrill

NEW ORLEANS is said to be one of the wicked cities of the world. It is said to be filled with adventurers and adventuresses. One thing I do know it is filled with: flowers, at a time of the year when all the rest of the continent is full of ice and snow and fog. Great big azalea bushes, bigger than lilac bushes, laden with azaleas—red, pink, salmon, rose. And gardenias and camellias, the kind the boy friends bring their girls singly in little boxes for a corsage when they are going to a party—down in New Orleans they hang on the bushes on streets, under the evergreen oaks. I know this, because I'm just back home from there.

As for wickedness, I couldn't find even a sample. But I did have one really good scare.

I was walking expectantly down one of those narrow little streets in what is called the Vieux Carre, or Old French Quarter. In most cities, these old districts become slums, and in due time, when they are condemned by the public health authorities, industry moves in and erects modern concrete and brick warehouses. But New Orleans is cagey. It has known about the tourist business for generations. People have been going down there for the flowers and fun for a hundred winters past. And what tourists like are wicked, old, narrow streets, with alleys leading into dim and palm-filled patios, where adventurers and adventuresses sit at little tables with flowered cotton table cloths, awaiting . . . whom?

However slowly I strolled, in the balmy March air, looking in all the antique-shop windows and tourist trinket booths, not one shady character could I detect. One party who appeared to my eye pretty depraved, and whom I followed three blocks, finally got into a car with an Ohio licence plate.

I was just beginning to feel cheated and cynical about the whole business when a slight, middle-aged man sidled up to me in the crowded narrow street and hissed in my ear:

"Hey! Take this! Just carry straight on, and I'll get it back from you in a minute."

And he shoved into my startled grasp a square cardboard carton about the size of a home-made bomb, a human head, or about $200,000 worth of smuggled dope.

As he shoved the box into my hands, he darted forward and walked ten feet ahead of me. My breath suddenly began to shorten. My heart thumped. I could feel it in my temples. When wickedness strikes, it strikes too fast for innocent characters like me. I thought of my dear wife, having her quiet afternoon snooze back at the motel on the city's outskirts. I thought of my name in the home-town newspapers—that is, if my body were ever found. I sneaked my hand into my wallet, remembering that my driving licence and identification cards were there. They would be able to tell who I was.

For a minute, I thought of tossing the box away and running in the reverse direction. I could soon lose myself in the throng of idle tourists jamming the narrow street. But at that instant, the man ahead turned a sinister face and made a swift signal, which either meant he wanted me to go slow, or that he was going to slit my throat.

Then he halted, and engaged in conversation with as grim-looking a woman as ever I saw. She was a chemical blonde, wearing a garish cotton dress, and was laden with gaudy costume jewelry. If ever I saw a run-down descendant of the Creoles of olden times, she was it.

She was staring tight-lipped at the slight man who had me in his power. Neither looked at me as I sidled by. I walked slowly on, feeling pins and needles, which are just as bad as daggers, in my back.

The slight man overtook me, and seized the box.

"Gosh, that was close!" he said, falling in step beside me. "An hour ago, my wife and I saw this genuine crystal vase in a store. Seventy-five bucks! They said it was out of an Old Southern Plantation home. But seventy-five bucks! I wouldn't let her buy it. She got mad. So later I pretended to go and get a shoe shine, and slipped back and bought it. I'm going to surprise her with it when we get back home. But just as I was passing you, I saw her in the crowd coming toward us . . ."

I felt the clammy pall of disillusion enfold me like a damp towel.

"Where you from?" I asked, in the best New Orleans accent.

"Winnipeg," said he.

Stood Up

TARDINESS drives me nuts. Some people are very patient. They will wait half an hour, or even longer, for a friend. They don't mind. They can just stand there, happy and content, watching the people coming in and out of a restaurant, or in a store lobby. Not me. I wouldn't wait fifteen minutes for the King of England or the Pope of Rome. Twenty minutes, maybe, for the Queen of England. But she is a lady.

I had waited fifteen minutes for a character named McLennan. We were to have lunch at this Italian restaurant, famous for its spaghetti, ravioli, rigatoni, tagliatelli and soup. It is no fun to stand in the lobby of an Italian restaurant with people pushing past you both in and out. Half of the people I knew by sight—newspapermen, magazine men, advertising men, artists, radio people, television people—you know the kind who go to Italian restaurants.

And they would look at me standing there slightly miffed and snooty, wondering who had stood me up. Well, it was this character McLennan who was standing me up. He always stands me up, though there is nothing personal in it. He stands everybody up.

But I love to have lunch with McLennan in an Italian restaurant. It is beautiful to watch him eat these Italian dishes. He doesn't even use a spoon to wind the stuff on his fork. With an airy grace, he dips his fork into the great, lithe heap, gives it a mysterious twirl, and up comes the most beautiful round mouthful of spaghetti wound on the fork, with not a single end dangling. He talks about literature, contemporary music, modern art, his eyes shining, with never a glance at his plate. And dip, twiddle, snick, up comes another neat, round undangling mouthful. I think there is Italian blood in him.

Well, at seventeen minutes past the appointed hour, I got so mad I stamped inside the restaurant and got a table away off in a corner. I ordered minestrone, the soup with the practically fresh vegetables floating in it, a soup nobody but Italians have ever thought of. And my usual order, rigatoni. Rigatoni is spaghetti rolled out in wide, flat ribbons, fairly thick, and cut short. You don't have to twiddle them. You can spear them, one at a time, or slide the fork under one of them. I ate the soup. The rigatoni came. It was now forty minutes past the appointed meeting. In the middle of the rigatoni, there was a commotion out in the hallway and at the door. People sitting near the door got up from their tables and looked out. I asked the waitress what the excitement was. An accident, she said. A guy bumped off by a car. Dead, she thought.

Well, I'm not on the police beat. I don't have to run after accidents any more. I sat eating rigatoni and watching with amusement the radio men, television men, artists, advertising men, with their table napkins in their hands, coming back in, all excited.

"Is it bad?" I asked one of them, as he passed my table.

"Wow!" he said. "The crazy guy. Running like mad right through traffic. Out here in front. Like I always say, people are nuts. Speed crazy. What's the hurry?"

I took him for an advertising man. As I pursued my helpless rigatoni about the plate, I could overhear snatches of the philosophic conversation around the tables. I glanced at my watch. It was now five minutes to the hour that McLennan had stood me up. Speed, they were saying. Crazy speed. Everybody rushing. Mad. The world is going nuts. I smiled at my last strip of rigatoni. But you can still be stood up.

At a quarter past two, I thought I would go to the pay phone and give this McLennan a small tasty piece of my mind. I called his office. I got his secretary.

"Is there a person by the name of McLennan works there?"

"Oh, Mr. Clark, haven't you heard?"

"Heard what?"

"Weren't you at the Italian restaurant?"

"Yes."

"Mr. McLennan was in an accident right out in front of it . . ."

"Is he dead?"

"No. They've got him in the emergency ward right now. He's got a broken arm. I thought you were with him."

"I waited seventeen minutes!" I said. "Did you hear? Seventeen minutes. And when he didn't come . . ."

"Oh, you know how he is, Mr. Clark."

"Which arm is broken?"

"His left, they told me."

I hung up. To take out, the Italian restaurant will put up spaghetti in insulated cartons. I got a carton of spaghetti Caruso, double portion, and a smaller carton of black Italian coffee espresso, which will make a man jump six feet in the air. I took these up to the hospital and found McLennan in bed in a small room off the emergency ward. We got a bed tray. He sat up and with his good arm ate the spaghetti. While he told me about the accident, his eyes shining, he dipped the fork, twiddle, snick, and up came the spaghetti in lovely round bites, not a vestige of dangle to it.

Such friends as you have got, you don't want to lose.

A Child Lost

IN A foreign country, you are likely to be more alert to the little things around you. I would probably not have noticed this man at all, back home here in Canada, or even in the States. But in the hotel lobby in Epernay, not far south of Rheims, he could hardly escape notice.

He was past middle age, was carefully dressed, had a fine, high-cheeked face; and he was literally frantic with anxiety. His face was flushed, and in his eyes was panic.

He must have been in and out the lobby three or four times before I really became aware of him. In the door he would come, stare a little wildly around; go to the dark alley leading into the check room; peer narrowly behind the racks. Then he would pass the caisse, where the clerk stood behind his counter, and open a door. There he poised, listening. Closing the door, he would run to the front door again and disappear.

No one in the lobby was paying the slightest attention to him. The half-dozen residents were slouched behind their Paris newspapers, tabloids. The clerk at the caisse never raised his eyes.

"The poor devil," I said to myself. "If he comes in again . . ."

He came in at that moment. He stared in agony all around the lobby, went to the entry of the check room . . .

"*Monsieur,*" I said, quietly sidling up to him, "*pardon! Puis-je vous assister?*"

I will tell the rest of the story in English instead of my corny French.

"Monsieur," gasped the gentleman with relief, "I've lost

a little boy! Have you seen a small boy about? Six years old? With fair . . ."

"Why, of course," I replied, taking his arm. "Just around to the west of the hotel here, only ten minutes ago."

"Thank God!" he cried, coming eagerly toward the door.

As we went out, I noticed the other people in the lobby had lowered their papers, and the clerk had turned his head to watch.

"Not ten minutes ago, Monsieur," I said, as we turned left, "a fine little boy on a tricycle. Would that be he? He has fair hair."

"Yes, yes, straight fair hair," gestured the distracted man, brushing with his hand.

"Exactly," I reassured him. "I thought when I saw him how like my own boy he looked. I have a little son of six."

We came to the arbor to the west of the hotel; and there was the small boy, wheeling his tricycle.

I pointed.

"No, no!" burst out the searcher, recoiling. "That's not Jacquot."

He pulled away from me and turned to run back toward the hotel entrance.

"Wait," I called. "Monsieur, look: you go around the far side, and I'll go up through the arbor here. How long has he been missing? Should we not look farther?"

He had paused to listen over his shoulder to me. Then he came back.

"It wasn't a moment ago!" he cried in white-faced terror. "I merely turned my back. He can't have got any distance."

"Then," I reassured him warmly, "you go around the far side of the hotel, I'll go up through here. Please don't panic. We'll find him."

"Thank you, thank you," gasped the poor devil, starting away.

Hmmmmmm! Two thousand, six hundred miles away, my boy, six. Two thousand, six hundred miles as the heart flies, as the arrow flies.

I hurried up through the arbor, watching. I came round the back of the hotel; asked the girls at the scullery door; turned the far side, and came back to the front entrance without meeting my friend.

When I entered the lobby, he was standing listening at the door at the back. The loungers were behind their tabloids, the clerk was bent at his counter.

"Pardon me," I said, a little crisply, to the clerk. "But that gentleman has lost a little boy. Could you suggest what we might do to assist him?"

The clerk had raised his eyes slowly to mine. Gravely.

"The little boy," he said softly, "has been lost a long time. Thirty years. Thirty-three years."

"I beg your pardon?" I leaned over.

"His little boy has been dead thirty some years," said the clerk.

The frenzied man swept past us, out the door.

"But," I cleared my throat, "but, surely, he doesn't go on like this? He'll kill himself! He is in a frenzy."

"Every few days," said the clerk, quietly, "he comes here and hunts for Jacquot. He has it in his mind that it was here, in this lobby, he let go the boy's hand."

I glanced around at the lobby. They went behind their tabloids. I walked softly and sat down on my chair.

As the heart flies, as the arrow flies!

Oh, arrows, arrows, arrows!

I hurried to my room. I took up the dinky little ivory telephone and asked the clerk at the desk to make a reservation for me on the bus which leaves Epernay at four, and to send a porter in half an hour for my bag.

That was how I came to Troyes at dark; and there bought one dozen postcards; on which I wrote fiercely, obscure nothings a little boy would understand; and kissed the stamps into place, and mailed them the 2,600 miles, straight as the heart flies, as the arrow flies; and went to my room, strange room, with no light lit, and trembled and wept.

Hazards

I CAN'T BEGIN to tell you how many times I have ordered the women in my house NEVER to put things on the stairs.

Little piles of newly-done ironing. Books. Parcels delivered, vacuum cleaners, cups of coffee. Things to go upstairs, later.

"We can't," they say, "be running up and down stairs all day."

"Well," I shout, "put them on a table, on the shelf, on top of the TV, any place!"

"We put them on the stairs," they explain, "so as not to forget them the next time we go up."

"NOT," I command, "on the stairs! Somebody is going to get killed around here, tripping on that stuff."

You see, I am an old soldier. Orders are orders and, as such, must be obeyed. Among the things old soldiers never do, besides dying, is learn that women won't take orders. Thus, when I come downstairs, I never look down. I walk boldly. I would hate to tell you how many times, in the last forty years, I have come within an inch of dusty death by tripping on things left on the stairs.

However, until last Tuesday I never really suffered any serious injury.

I came home at noon, for a pleasant afternoon off. I intended to isolate myself up in my den and re-arrange my trout flies, tie a couple of dozen fresh nylon leaders, read Haig-Brown's *The Western Angler,* paste up a new survey map I had bought of the Chicoutimi country, on window-blind linen, and generally get in shape for any trout-fishing trips that the next few weeks might provide.

"The McDoodles," announced my wife, "are coming for tea this afternoon."

"Aw, NO!" I moaned.

The McDoodles consist of Mr. and Mrs. McDoodle, Mr. McDoodle's sister, Ag, and Mrs. McDoodle's sister, Jenn. They travel in a pack.

My womenfolk are very fond of the McDoodles. Their effect, on arriving anywhere, is to set off an acoustic bomb. Everybody talks at once. The whole house shakes with the sound of them all, me included, whooping and hollering, and nobody listening. It goes on for hours.

"Ladies," I announced, chill and acid, "I wish you to understand that I am in Montreal."

"Now, now, Greg!" they all expostulated.

"I will be up in my room, quietly at work," I stated levelly, "with the door shut. I won't make a sound. But you understand? I am in Montreal!"

"Awwww!" they all said.

At about a quarter to four P.M., the McDoodles arrived. I could hear them as they parked out in front. It was like the faint, far gaggle of wild geese. When they came up the front walk and to the door, it was like the passage of a flight of a hundred. I heard my front door open. And the acoustic bomb exploded. My house burst.

Leaving a crack of my door open, I listened.

"Where's Greg?" inquired McDoodle, like a mushroom cloud.

"We're so sorry!" I heard my womenfolk cry. "Greg's in Montreal for the week. Big editorial conference . . ."

"Awwww!" cried all the McDoodles, like the fall-out.

So I closed the crack of the door very, very gently, and tiptoed back to my rocking chair, where I had the trout-fly boxes all set out on other chairs, and my coils of nylon for leaders, and Haig-Brown's beautiful book, and the new map, and the mucilage, and the window-blind linen.

Ah, it was kindly to sit there in the peace and quiet, amid all these lares and penates, which is Latin for household or personal gods; and listen, with an inner sweet sense of guilt, to the distant tumult downstairs. For fear McDoodle or one of his women might come upstairs and snoop, the way people do when visiting, I went and locked my door.

About 5:15, the smell of coffee sneaked in under the crack of the door, together with toasty smells, suggesting toasted cheese sandwiches, and maybe bacon and little-pig sausages spiked on toothpicks, not to mention cinnamon toast.

(Now the stage darkens.)

I tiptoed over and unlocked the door. I listened. The racket downstairs had reached the 5:15 crescendo. There was nobody upstairs. I opened the door and tiptoed across the hall.

As you might suppose, I live in an old-fashioned house. It has, among other things, a back staircase. I call it the escape hatch. It leads down to the kitchen.

I peered down the dim staircase. Not a sound came up. Nobody was in the kitchen. Yet doubtless there would be the odd few sandwiches, little-pig sausages, curls of bacon on toothpicks, not to mention cinnamon toast, left lying about.

The door at the bottom of the back stairs was closed. Though it occasioned darkness and low visibility on the stairs, it still afforded me a sort of last protection, in case any McDoodles were in the kitchen, snooping for little-pig sausages, or . . .

I crept down the back stairs. I felt my way along the wall with my hand.

I put my foot, my right foot, into my own great big bushel-size, khaki-japanned, tin waste basket, which some woman had taken down and emptied, and then, in defiance of my life-long orders, had set on the stairs to take up the next time she felt like it.

The racket was something dreadful.

The bushel-size waste basket teeters on ordinary stairs. It teetered the moment I sank my foot into it, and over I went. When I hit the door at the bottom, it gave. In addition to the noise the tin basket was making were those sounds naturally to be expected from a man, an old soldier, who all his life had counselled against the sources of this very evil which was now befalling him. Besides which, a man taken in a moment of stealth, like that, is almost bound to utter a few uncontrollable howls and roars. They come instinctively.

Well, of course, it was idle of me to suppose, as I landed out on the kitchen floor, that the tumult in the living room would drown out all other sound. In a matter of seconds, all my womenfolk and all the McDoodles were in the kitchen, milling around me.

McDoodle helped me pull the waste basket off my foot.

"I just got in from Montreal," I explained, as they helped me to my feet, "on the afternoon train, see? And when I saw there was company in the house, I just thought I would sneak in up the back way, and get freshened up."

It worked.

But I figure it was a lesson to the womenfolk.

It's a Very Small World

THE TEATRO ANTICO in Taormina, Sicily, is the very beautiful antique ruins of a theatre built by the Greeks at the height of their civilization, while Rome was still a bunch of Bolsheviks back in the hills, and Sicily was a tourist resort for the Athenians.

I was up in the top gallery, leaning on the stone parapet with Ralph Allen, Bill Stewart and a couple of other war correspondents watching through our field glasses while the British Navy's monitors, with sixteen-inch guns, pasted the poor little town of Reggio, on the toe of Italy, where we landed four days later to find no Germans, but only an enthusiastic throng of thunderstricken Italians, glad to see us.

BOING! would go the sixteen-inchers: we would swivel our glasses on to Reggio: POWEE! would go the slow, great fountains of dust and ruin.

But I couldn't keep my mind on the monitors. I turned around. There, calm in the luminous Sicilian sunlight, lay at my feet the spacious amphitheatre, a full circle of tier upon tier of stone seats, with aisles and loges and boxes just like our finest theatres. And the focus of it, the stage, raised, with its plentiful backstage space for wings and props and performers. Twenty-three centuries had failed to obliterate the shape and form of it. I suppose the stone, when Aeschylus was played here as new as Christopher Fry, was faced with marble, and the higher-priced seats were cushioned with purple. Here, up in the gods, we likely brought our own cushions. Aeschylus, Euripides, the Shakespeares and Bernard Shaws of their day; and how many flops and one-night stands?

BOING! POWIE! There goes another sixteen-incher into Reggio. But then the Greeks faded out and the Romans took over, and Sicily became a tourist resort for the new imperialists, and the Roman gauleiters had villas here in and about Taormina and the theatre filled up with summer stock, and people interested in culture, Roman culture, and the advancements of the arts, would swarm in here, chatty, gushy, recognizing one another gaily. Horace came down here from Rome on regular lecture tours and read his witty poems. In person. Quintus Horatius Flaccus, in person.

Of course, in addition to the regular runs of legitimate theatre, they would also have had local celebrations— choirs, ballet, or whatever they called ballet then. In the morning sunlight, I began to clothe the ancient stones with marble and with cushions, and to people it. BOING! POWIE! There goes another into Reggio.

"Hey," said Ralph Allen. "Turn around here. Look at that one, smack in the middle of the town . . ."

But I was just at the point of having the doors opened and the first of the togaed crowd in the queue come swarming through that far entrance, there, to the left of the stage, when, somewhat to my chagrin, through that very entrance came a bevy of about eight or ten young American soldiers.

American soldiers can look sloppier than almost any soldiers in the world. But they can also look prettiest, when they are in their walking-out kit, with their smart tunics, their "pinks," which are slacks of a sort of pastel khaki; and their wedge caps worn forward on their heads, and their invariable little expensive cameras slung open across their chests. Shoes bright, too.

These boys were all in their best. They swarmed around the stage, gazing raptly up at the wide and lovely amphitheatre. Across the distance, I could hear their voices distinctly. BOING! POWIE! Another sixteen-incher.

So down the long descent I went, tier to tier, row to row, disturbing the lizards and the dust.

I joined the kids.

"Fantastic, isn't it?" they said. "Fabulous." "Gee."

"Miss Adams, mah history teacher," said one, with a fine Texas drawl, "will get a big kick when I write her about this. She's told me about it. This identical theatre. I'll send her some snaps."

They were climbing up on the stone stage, striking attitudes, declaiming.

"You're from Texas, aren't you?" I asked.

"Yes, suh."

"What part?"

"Midland, suh. That's in West Texas."

"Midland?" I checked.

"Yes, suh, Midland."

I studied him in astonishment. He would be about the same age as Murray Fasken, my nephew, Capt. Murray Fasken of the First American Cavalry, at that moment somewhere in or near the Philippines.

"Do you," I hesitated, "by any chance know Murray Fasken?"

"Murray?" he exclaimed. "I surely do. We went to school together, and then to college. Why, I sure do know Murray Fasken."

"He's my nephew," I explained, holding out my hand, and we shook.

So, instead of getting Horace in my mind's eye there, in his toga, freshly barbered, and probably with some make-up on, reciting O Fons Bandusiae from the stage to the cushioned multitude up the sloping amphitheatre in the

— 177 —

limpid Sicilian sunlight, I got from Texas the chum of my nephew somewhere in, or near, the Philippines . . .

BOING! POWIE!

I looked up the ancient terraced tiers, far up, where Allen and the others were leaning, their backs to me, on the parapet of the gods.

Small world, old, old world, full of people we know.

The Cowboy

MOTORING through Texas lately with some friends, we were struck by the absence of cowboys in this last stronghold of the breed.

We saw plenty of big hats with wide, upflaring brims; plenty of skin-tight blue jeans, and any number of fancy-stitched cowboy boots with high heels. But on inquiry, we discovered that, without exception, those wearing the authentic outfits were tourists from New York and the New England states. This dissuaded me, in San Antonio, from buying a very fine cowboy hat I could have got for only $8.

What we did find in Texas were oilmen. The Lone Star state is full of oilmen, and a more unromantic crew you would never want to see. They are toilers, wearing small safety hats not unlike undersize steel helmets. A far cry from the ten-gallon hat. It seems Texas isn't interested in ten gallons any more. Everything is by the barrel. A hundred, two hundred barrels a day; that's what they are interested in.

Far west of San Antonio, we pulled into a little highway snack bar, wide on the lone Texas range. Seated inside were a few dowdy gentlemen in khaki trousers and shirts, wearing ordinary old felt hats that looked as if they had been sat on instead of worn, most of the time.

They were not bow-legged from riding cayuses. They were knock-kneed, from riding in jeeps. The cowhand of today rides herd in jeeps or sometimes in Cadillacs, depending on whether there is oil as well as cattle on his ranch.

They eyed us respectfully as we came in. They ceased their conversation and lowered their eyes modestly. There was a spinsterish look about them all.

"Know something?" I murmured to my companions, as we sat down at a table. "I bet you we are at last in the presence of cowboys!"

My friends, glancing pleasantly about the little snack bar, covertly inspected the half-dozen dusty, drab gentlemen of varied ages and sizes at the far end.

"Pah!" they said: "Cowboys?"

They had that sand-blasted rather than tanned look that outdoor Texans wear. But the impression of old-maidishness about them, a kind of withery, prim quality, was what I was going by, in my guess. For, having listened all these years to cowboy songs, those melancholy, wailing, lonely yodels and whines that are identified with this classic breed of men, I cannot help but know that real cowboys are moody and modest men bearing little resemblance to the cowboy of fiction and the movies.

"Want to bet?" I asked my friends.

A small bet, sufficient to pay me the price of a pair of skin-tight Levis, was agreed upon.

"Excuse me, gentlemen," I said, going over to the other table, "but we're strangers here. We're playing a little game called 'What's My Line?' I say you're cowhands. Is that right?"

They all smiled delightedly.

"That's right, suh," they chorused in their mild, Texas way. "We-all work on this ranch heah, on the both sides of the hahway."

"Horses?" I inquired. "You got horses outside?"

"Hosses?" checked the oldest of them, a wiry little tenor of about sixty-five. "Not heah, suh. We got some hosses back at headquarters, that's about thirty miles from heah. But mostly, we do our ranching by cah."

"Cah?"

"Jeeps," he explained, "pickups, cahs."

— 180 —

"I figure hosses," put in a very tall, lean youth, a baritone, "would scare our caows. Panic them, maybe."

"Cattle," submitted the bass-baritone, a middle-aged man who looked like ZaSu Pitts, "is used to cahs."

I thanked them, and went back and collected fifty cents all round my table.

At this moment, the door opened and in strode a terrific apparition. Six feet four, lean as an axe handle, his slender legs snug in skin-tight Levis, he was the picture of the cowboy, not of fiction but of dreams. He had a great silver-gray hat on, its crown rising like a quart sealer, its brim vast and upcurled on both sides. His boots were scarlet and tan, in arabesque design, stitched with white; and heels four inches high.

To my astonishment, he was greeted warmly and respectfully by all the cowhands. He was no tourist from Brooklyn or Toronto! As he strode past the cowhands, he patted a couple on the back, ruffled a head or two, and then went to the counter and took a stool in front of the bright-eyed waitress.

My friends closed in on me. They held out their hands for their fifty cents.

"Aha!" they whispered. "The boss! The head wrangler! Now you *are* seeing your first real cowboy."

I do not let go money that easy.

I sneaked over to my friends, the cowhands.

"Who's he?" I hissed.

"The local school teachah," they hissed back.

The Hint

MR. JOE GREAVES is a respected member of the newspaper printing trade in Port Arthur. But twenty years ago, he was Pte. Joe Greaves.

And one day the sergeant-major said to him: "What's your line?"

"Driver," offered Joe. "Jeeps, trucks, lorries."

"Civil life?" checked the S.M.

"Printer," said Joe. "Newspaper."

"Ha!" said the S.M.

And that is how Joe was instructed to report himself forthwith to the Public Relations unit of the First Canadian Division, which was fighting in Italy.

And that is how Joe found himself driving a jeep with me in the back seat.

Now, I am going to make this story as respectful of myself as I can. After all, a man at my age owes himself a little consideration. Sitting there in the back seat of the jeep, I was fifty-one years old, which is pretty creaky in war time, even for a war correspondent. To keep up with kids of nineteen or twenty-three, with colonels only twenty-five years of age, and brigadiers twenty-nine, you have got to be nimble.

Nimble in the wits, if not in the joints. To begin with, I had one advantage: I had been an army officer in the previous war, and had several medal ribbons brightening up my ill-fitting battle dress. I used to carry my left chest a little forward of my right chest when dealing with these young strangers. They had no ribbons yet.

And further to confuse them, I had another heritage from the first war. In that famous war, I had been scared right up to the edge of my steel helmet, with the result that, while my hair under the helmet stayed brown, my side hair turned white. And by growing these white sideburns luxuriantly, I found I could create a sort of Foxy Grandpa image that puzzled the young soldiers sorely. Until they saw my green - and - gold "War Correspondent" insignia on my shoulders, they might suppose I was the Episcopal Bishop of Ohio, or perhaps the general's uncle. Many a sentry, seeing me approach, would get the spasms trying to decide whether to give me a mere butt salute, a present arms, or to turn out the guard. Nothing like a good bunch of white sidewhiskers in war time.

Pte. Joe Greaves, on first seeing me sitting plump in the back seat of the jeep he was destined to drive for many a thousand mile in the Italian mountains, was duly impressed and confused. To add to his confusion, he told me afterwards, I reminded him of his Grandpa.

Joe was three things above all: a skilled and daring driver, a joyous laugher, and a most gentle heart.

But he hadn't driven me more than ten miles before he made the horrifying discovery that he had with him perhaps the worst back-seat driver in the world.

Capt. Gordon Hutton, M.C., of Vancouver, who was our conducting officer, and sat in the front seat of the jeep beside Joe, put it into the official records that he had, in his previous experience, encountered some two hundred back-seat drivers, and that I was as bad as all the two hundred put together.

It may be so. But, as I told them over and over, after all, God made me. Joe loved driving, and a jeep, to a young soldier, was something like a sports car. He didn't own it. He didn't have to pay for its upkeep. Boy!

And here were the mountain roads of Italy, hairpin turns, obstacles, vast abysses without rails to lend spice to every twist and turn . . .

But in the back seat, the champion back-seat driver of the world, a feeble, cantankerous old gentleman who reminded him of his grandfather, and who roused in Joe's gentle and respectful nature every sentiment of consideration . . .

It was a cruel situation. And with lively interest, I set myself to watch it work itself out.

At every burst of speed down a mountain road, I bellowed. At every turn, I shouted caution. If we raced too close into the dust cloud of a ten-ton truck's tail, I howled. Uphill, I demanded the jeep's double-low gear. Downhill, I pleaded.

Joe's happy laughter died. In a few days, his weight began to fall. In the mornings, he came slowly to his job. In the evenings, when he let me out at my quarters, he raced away in flying cinders. Captain Hutton watched us out of the corner of his eye.

High in the sad, agonized mountains of Molise, where surely no poet ever sang, we were hop-skip-and-jeeping over disaster-riven mountain roads and I was practically popping, when there suddenly, on a jagged turn, appeared before us the smoking wreckage of a lorry that had struck a ratchet mine a little while before. It was strewn all over the narrow road and up the steep mountainside.

Joe Greaves jammed the brakes and we crept up on the gruesome spectacle.

Joe locked the hand brake, bailed out. Up the steep bank he scrambled and started wrestling in the wreckage.

Down he bounded, bearing in his hands the steering wheel of the lorry and a broken bit of its column.

He hoisted them over the side of the jeep into my lap.

"There!" he cried triumphantly. "Now you can drive too!"